£3·25

Maths f

Su

M/
Lecturer in Mathematical Education
University of Warwick

Baillière Tindall

LONDON PHILADELPHIA TORONTO SYDNEY TOKYO

Baillière Tindall   24–28 Oval Road
W. B. Saunders   London NW1 7DX, England

The Curtis Center
Independence Square West
Philadelphia, PA 19106–3399, USA

1 Goldthorne Avenue
Toronto, Ontario M8Z 5T9, Canada

Harcourt Brace Jovanovich Group
(Australia) Pty Ltd
32–52 Smidmore Street
Marrickville, NSW 2204, Australia

Harcourt Brace Jovanovich Japan Inc.
Ichibancho Central Building, 22–1 Ichibancho
Chiyoda-ku, Tokyo 102, Japan

First published 1985
Reprinted 1989

Typeset by Photo·Graphics, Honiton, Devon
Printed and bound in Great Britain by
Richard Clay Ltd, Bungay, Suffolk

British Library Cataloguing in Publication Data

Pirie, Susan
  Maths for nursing.
  1. Nursing—Mathematics
  I. Title
  510′.24613   RT68

ISBN 0–7020–1091–X (Paperback)
ISBN 0–7020–1092–8 (Calculator pack)

Contents

Acknowledgements

I would like to express my gratitude to all those learners, nurses and tutors who gave me so much valuable help with the research which has led to the publication of this book.

My especial thanks, however, must go to the learners who were my guinea-pigs at Bath and Brighton Schools of Nursing.

Foreword

Mathematical error in nursing practice can cost lives, and on occasions this has actually been the case.

I will begin by making a confession: in numerical terms I have always been semi-literate. I have vivid memories of numbers holding sheer terror for me as a young child. None of my maths teachers ever quite had the ability to unlock the mysteries of numbers for me. I remember all too well feeling humiliated by an exasperated maths teacher who had tried for the umpteenth time to make my simple mind understand the wonders of different formulae. I am afraid that his wisdom was lost completely where I was concerned!

On entering nursing I quickly realised that numbers and I would have to come to terms with each other—the process was exceedingly painful. I remember grappling with basic maths in a variety of settings and having drug calculations checked and re-checked to satisfy my neurosis about numbers. There were no opportunities for remedial teaching in an already packed programme.

Here at last we have a book written for people like me. Dr Pirie has prepared a text that is logical, readable and, above all, understandable and relevant to real-life nursing situations. For the numerate, the book provides an ideal aid to teaching, since it is based on the principle of self-study, and this kind of learning is destined to 'stick'.

The style of this book is such that learning about maths need not be a chore—it can be fun. The book is also designed to allow you to go at your own pace. Heed the advice of the author by taking a break between sections.

If you cannot master a section, take heart, have a rest and return to try again at a later stage. I tried this approach in relation to SI units, and it works.

Some maths in nursing is complex, which is hardly surprising given the ever increasing number of drugs available in modern health care. This book will prepare you for almost all clinical situations, so read it, enjoy it and use what it has to say on the ward—this is what it has been written for.

In commending this book to you, I can only wish that it had been written many years before—it would have saved me a lot of worry.

Ray Rowden   April 1985
SRN, RMN, OncNC, MBIM

Ray Rowden is Professional Officer at the RCN Association of Nursing Management and Honorary Lecturer in the Department of Nursing at the Royal Marsden Hospital, London. He is also author of *Managing Nursing* published by Baillière Tindall.

How to Use this Book

This book is the result of a three-year research project exploring the deficiencies in basic mathematical skills among nurses. The findings show that large numbers of learners, and indeed nurses themselves, have problems with some of the aspects of mathematics needed for their daily work. However elementary your difficulties, you are not alone. There is no need to feel embarrassed provided you are prepared to do something to remedy your weaknesses. This book will help you to do this.

Remember, if an engineer miscalculates, time and valuable materials may be wasted—if a nurse miscalculates, a patient may die.

There were three phases to the research project mentioned above. The first identified the mathematics which a nurse needs on the job. The second discovered which of these mathematical areas cause problems for nurses. The third considered various forms of help which could be offered to nurses to enable them to function safely and efficiently. The project was concerned with only that mathematics which was essential to practising nurses—as opposed to that which would be good for their souls! Practical considerations, too, insisted that the remedy offered had to be capable of being absorbed into an already full school of nursing timetable. There seemed little point in proving that six two-hour sessions of private tuition would deal with a nurse's mathematical inadequacies since no school of nursing would be either able or willing to devote this amount of time to the problem.

Around 1000 nurses and learners took part in the research and experiments showed that by far the most effective method of enabling learners to achieve mastery in the necessary mathematics was through the use of five self-help booklets written specifically for nurses.

These booklets have been combined to form part of this book. The teaching is by means of a programmed learning approach in which small sections of work are presented in a simple logical sequence. Each unit is designed to help you with a particular difficulty in the sort of mathematics you need as a nurse and can be rapidly mastered if the suggestions below are followed.

You will need a pencil and paper.

Each section is followed by a few straightforward questions. Answer these on paper (not in the book) and turn to the end of the unit to check your answers. If all your answers are correct, carry on to the next section. If not, go back over the text carefully and then try the check test again. Do not move on until you have mastered the section.

Do not try to do more than three or four sections and their checks without a break. Five or 10 minutes (or even two days!) rest will help to 'fix' what you have already learned and restore your powers of concentration. If you feel that you are floundering or getting bogged down, **stop**. Go away and come back later when you are feeling calmer and ready to try again.

In addition to the five teaching units, there is an introductory test to enable you to see what your problems really are. You are strongly urged to do the test since the research indicates that nearly 50% of learners overestimate their mathematical abilities.

'How to use your calculator', however, is the place to start. This section explains all you need to know about the use of your new nurse's calculator. It has been designed to be small enough to go in your pocket and therefore to be with you whenever you need it. You may have used a calculator before. Even if you have, you need to skim through this section since there may be features on the nurse's calculator which make it different from the machines that you are used to. You are of course not obliged to use a calculator when working through the units. It is given to you simply as an aid, to use when you feel it appropriate.

When you complete each unit's final check successfully you can feel confident that you have now mastered another of the skills needed to enable you to be a safe, responsible nurse. **But** everyone is fallible and there is no substitute for asking yourself after **every** calculation, however pressured you may feel: **Is that a reasonable answer?**

How to Use your Calculator

Before you go any further with this book, you need to become familiar with your calculator. Calculators come in a variety of shapes, colours, sizes and, more important, a variety of ways of working. It is essential that you work through this chapter with your new calculator even, or perhaps especially, if you have used a calculator before.

Calculators do not think—you have to do that. They will merely perform the calculating tasks you set them, in the way that they have been manufactured to work. You need, therefore, to know the correct instructions to give in order to get the answer you want.

Some of the buttons are self-evident: [off], the numbers, [=], [÷], [+], [×], [−] are what you would expect. [on c%] turns the calculator on, and [.] is the decimal point.

From time to time throughout this book you will come across *key sequences*. These tell you exactly which buttons to press and the order in which to press them. For example:

To calculate 25×0.3, use key sequence [off][on][2][5][×] [0][.][3][=]

Always press [off][on] before beginning each new calculation. This is not necessary in every case, but **safety** is of more importance than speed in any calculation that you do, and this key sequence ensures that you do not unknowingly include numbers from a previous calculation. It is always a wise precaution to do every calculation twice, especially when dealing with drug doses. Mistakes can be fatal.

Before reading further, work through the following set of calculations just to get your fingers used to the feel and position of the buttons:

Exploration 1

Key sequence

1) 2.5 + 6.3   `off` `on` `2` `.` `5` `+` `6` `.` `3` `=`

2) 7.4 + 12.3 + 9.1

`off` `on` `7` `.` `4` `+` `1` `2` `.` `3` `+` `9` `.` `1` `=`

3) 44 × 9

4) 155 ÷ 5

5) 86 ÷ 40

6) 1793 − 846

7) 2222 + 3335

8) 1234 × 4321

9) 9876 ÷ 123

10) 5.03 − 0.07

11) 0.06 × 0.31

12) 2.804 ÷ 0.2

13) Add together 17, 19, 16, 18, 21, 17, 19

14) Add together 0.3, 0.71, 1.26, 0.04, 2.03

15) Add together 276, 139, 5404, 72, 6161, 35

You may have found yourself accidentally pressing the wrong keys occasionally. What did you do? Many people heave a sigh, switch the calculator off and start all over again. Fortunately this is not necessary on this model. Try the following and note the answer you get. Can you see what the calculator is doing?

Exploration 2   Comments

1) [off] [on] [7] [−] [×] [2] [=]
2) [off] [on] [6] [+] [÷] [3] [=]
3) [off] [on] [6] [÷] [+] [3] [=]
4) [off] [on] [9] [+] [−] [5] [=]
5) [off] [on] [4] [+] [6] [−] [÷] [5] [=]
6) [off] [on] [3] [×] [8] [×] [−] [7] [=]
7) [off] [on] [7] [+] [−] [6] [+] [÷] [5] [=]

As you probably spotted the calculator works with whatever *function key* (+, −, ×, ÷) you pressed last, so wrong functions are automatically erased by pressing the key you want, but previous numbers and calculations are not affected.

What happens if you press the wrong number key? Clearly just pressing the correct number will not work: [2] then [5] gives 25. Try the following, note what answer you get and comment on what is happening.

Exploration 3   Comments

1) [off] [on] [2] [on] [5] [=]
2) [off] [on] [3] [on] [4] [+] [1] [=]
3) [off] [on] [7] [+] [3] [on] [4] [=]
4) [off] [on] [4] [×] [3] [on] [5] [−] [7] [=]
5) [off] [on] [5] [−] [2] [on] [3] [+] [4] [=]
6) [off] [on] [6] [−] [4] [×] [3] [on] [+] [9] [=]
7) [off] [on] [5] [−] [2] [×] [4] [on] [+] [3] [=]
8) [off] [on] [5] [−] [2] [×] [4] [+] [on] [3] [=]
9) [off] [on] [8] [−] [6] [×] [3] [+] [on] [9] [=]
10) [off] [on] [3] [on] [5]
11) [4] [+] [6] [on] [1] [=]

The effect of the [on] button pressed directly after a number is to erase that number without affecting any of the previous working. If you press [on] directly after a function key, however, you do lose everything.

If you **want** to *clear* everything and start again, the [off][on] sequence is the best way of doing so.

The way a calculator actually performs its calculations is called its *logic* and it is because this feature varies from one model to another that you need to read this section carefully.

Before you use your calculator write down what you think the answer will be to the following calculations, then press the buttons and see:

Exploration 4

Calculate	Guess	Press
1) $2 + 3 \times 4$		
2) $3 \times 4 + 2$		
3) $5 + 1 \times 4$		
4) $4 \times 1 + 5$		
5) $7 - 3 \times 2$		
6) $7 + 1 \div 2$		
7) $8 \div 2 + 5$		
8) $9 \div 2 + 1$		

The nurse's calculator has what is called *arithmetic logic* and therefore does each calculation as it goes along, in the order that you press the buttons. Most of the time this is just what you would want to happen, but problems arise when you have fractions.

The fraction ½ means $1 \div 2$. Do $\boxed{1}\boxed{\div}\boxed{2}\boxed{=}$ on your calculator and you get 0.5 (you probably already knew that ½ = 0.5). **But** now try $\boxed{3}\boxed{+}\boxed{1}\boxed{\div}\boxed{2}\boxed{=}$ The answer is 2 not 3½! This is because the calculator did $3 + 1 = 4$ first instead of $1 \div 2 = 0.5$.

It is thus very important to remember to do fractions first and store the answer before doing a string of computations. This is dealt with more fully in Unit 3 on formulae, which is where the problem may arise.

There are other occasions, too, when you may want to remember part of a calculation—there is a *memory* in your calculator for just this purpose.

Exploration 5

Switch your calculator off and then on again. The *display* (window) shows 0. on the right hand side.

Now press $\boxed{5}$ and the display changes to 5.

Now press $\boxed{\text{M+}}$. A small M has appeared in the top left corner of the display to indicate that you have just added something, in this case 5, to the memory store.

Press $\boxed{\text{on}}$. This clears the 5 from the display, but the M remains to remind you that the memory store is no longer empty. Now press $\boxed{2}$ $\boxed{\text{M+}}$. What do you expect to find in the store? Press $\boxed{\text{MRC}}$ *(memory recall)* to find out. The answer is 7 because a running total of $5 + 2$ has been formed in the store.

[MRC] will display the content of the memory, but will also leave the number in store.

Using [M−] will subtract numbers from the store. Try [on] [3] [M−] [MRC] .

One important thing to remember, is to check that the memory is empty when you start a new calculation. If you have the 'M' in the display, then the memory is not empty and you need to press [MRC] [MRC] (i.e. twice) to clear it. Switching the machine off also clears the memory.

Work through the following:

Exploration 6

1) [off] [on] [5] [+] [2] [M+] [1] [+] [MRC] [=]
2) [off] [on] [8] [−] [6] [M+] [4] [+] [MRC] [=]
3) [off] [on] [7] [−] [3] [M+] [8] [+] [MRC] [=]
4) [off] [on] [7] [M+] [2] [M+] [5] [M+] [MRC]
5) [off] [on] [4] [M+] [3] [M−] [6] [M+] [MRC]
6) [off] [on] [8] [M+] [2] [M−] [3] [M−] [1] [M+] [MRC]
7) [off] [on] [5] [M+] [2] [×] [MRC] [=]
8) [3] [×] [MRC] [=]
9) [7] [+] [MRC] [=]
10) [6] [−] [MRC] [=]

Together with percentages (%), which are dealt with in Unit 4, this is all you need to know as a working nurse about your new calculator. If, however, you wish to explore this calculator further there is an appendix at the end of the book to help you.

To familiarise yourself with your new calculator use it to do lots of easy calculations. Play with it when shopping. Find an old arithmetic book and do some of the exercises. Use it as often as possible so that you can use it automatically when you need it on the ward.

From time to time you will see, in the units, key sequences suggested for calculations you could do in your head. These are merely there to help you become familiar with your calculator.

Now read on, to become a safe nurse for whom mathematics holds no terrors!

Answers

Exploration 1

1) 8.8
2) 28.8
3) 396
4) 31
5) 2.15
6) 947
7) 5557
8) 5332114
9) 80.292682
10) 4.96
11) 0.0186
12) 14.02
13) 127
14) 4.34
15) 12087

Exploration 2

1) 14   i.e. 7×2
2) 2   i.e. $6 \div 3$
3) 9   i.e. $6 + 3$
4) 4   i.e. $9 - 5$
5) 2   i.e. $4 + 6 = 10$ then $10 \div 5 = 2$
6) 17   i.e. $3 \times 8 = 24$ then $24 - 7 = 17$
7) 0.2   i.e. $7 - 6 = 1$ then $1 \div 5 = 0.2$

Exploration 3

Comments

1) 5   `2` `on` cleared the display to 0
2) 5   `3` `on` cleared the display to 0. Then $4 + 1 = 5$
3) 11   `3` `on` left $7 +$ in the machine, producing $7 + 4 = 11$
4) 13   `3` `on` left $4 \times$ in the machine producing $4 \times 5 = 20$. Then $20 - 7 = 13$
5) 6   `2` `on` left $5 -$ in the machine producing $5 - 3 = 2$. Then $2 + 4 = 6$

6) 11 $\boxed{\times}$ $\boxed{3}$ $\boxed{on}$ $\boxed{+}$ leaves $6 - 4 = 2$ in the machine, changes 3 back to this 2 and changes $\times$ to $+$. Then $2 + 9 = 11$

7) 6 $\boxed{\times}$ $\boxed{4}$ $\boxed{on}$ $\boxed{+}$ leaves $5 - 2 = 3$ in the machine, changes 4 back to this 3 and changes $\times$ to $+$. Then $3 + 3 = 6$

8) 3 $\boxed{+}$ $\boxed{on}$ results in all the previous calculation being lost!

9) 9 $\boxed{+}$ $\boxed{on}$ results in all the previous calculation being lost!

10) 5 $\boxed{on}$ replaces 3 by 5

11) 55   No $\boxed{off}$ $\boxed{on}$ at the start left the 5 from the previous question in the display to form $54 + 1 = 55!$

Exploration 4

1) 20
2) 14
3) 24
4) 9
5) 8
6) 4
7) 9
8) 5.5

Exploration 5

1) 8
2) 6
3) 12
4) 14
5) 7
6) 4
7) 10
8) 15 ⎫
9) 12 ⎬ These are all working on the 5 left in the memory from
10) 1 ⎭ part 7.
      No $\boxed{off}$ $\boxed{on}$ sequence has been used to clear the memory.

Introductory Test

This test is in five parts, to correspond with the five teaching units in this book. Before you start to read the book, work through the whole test.

If you do not have 6/6 for every section, don't despair. You now know where your mathematical weaknesses lie and working through the relevant units will enable you to acquire the skills you need.

Unit 1. Test on SI Units

1) 1.5 kg = [   ] g

   52 g = [   ] kg

2) 4.56 micrograms = [   ] mg

   0.72 mg = [   ] micrograms

3) 180 mm = [   ] m

   7.6 m = [   ] mm

4) 75 μl = [   ] ml

   20 ml = [   ] μl

5) 1 mega unit of penicillin = [   ] units

   4184 joules = [   ] kilojoules

6) Put the following into the boxes below in order of size starting with the largest.

   1 mg, 1 g, 1 Mg, 1 μg, 1 kg

   [   ] [   ] [   ] [   ] [   ]

Unit 2. Test on Drug Doses

1) Nicoumalone, an anticoagulant, comes in 4 mg tablets. A doctor prescribes 10 mg for a patient with a thrombosis. How many pills must the patient have?

2) A patient needs 25 mg of a drug, injected every four hours. The drug is dispensed in ampoules containing 50 mg in one ml. How many ampoules are used for each injection?

3) Papaveretum, an opium injection, is available as a 20 mg per ml solution. How many ml will be given to a 10-year-old child prescribed 5 mg?

4) A doctor prescribes a dose of 30 units of soluble insulin. The available stock is of strength 100 units/ml. How many ml will the patient be given?

5) 5 ml of syrup contain 500 micrograms of a drug. How much syrup does a patient need to be given in order to receive 0.5 mg of the drug?

6) 12 mg of trimeprazine tartrate, an oral premedication, are to be given to a child. It is available as a syrup dose in 30 mg per 5 ml strength. How much of the syrup must the child have?

Unit 3. Test on Formulae

1) The rate of petrol consumption is given by the formula:

$$\text{Rate} = \frac{\text{Miles}}{\text{Gallons}}$$

The car has gone 228 miles and used 6 gallons of petrol. Find the consumption rate.

2) Given $\dfrac{3a}{b} = c$, where a = 48 and b = 6, find c.

3) Daily fluid requirement in ml = 150 × Weight in kg. How much does a baby aged 10 weeks and weighing 4.1 kg need?

4) You are told that:

$$\text{The amount you need} = \frac{\text{Strength you want}}{\text{Strength available}}$$

If the bottle has a solution strength 600 mg per ml, and you want 1 ml of solution strength 400 mg per ml, how much solution do you need from the bottle?

5) No. of pills dispensed = No. of pills per first dose × No. of doses × No. of days + No. of pills per second dose × No. of doses × No. of days

The doctor prescribes 2 pills three times a day for 7 days followed by 1 pill twice a day for 5 days. How many pills must the pharmacist dispense?

6) A baby's expected weight (kg) = Birth weight (kg) + (Age in weeks − 2) × 0.2

How much should a 2-month-old baby weigh now if her birth weight was 3.1 kg?

Unit 4. Test on Percentages

1) 5% of 1 =

2) 2% of 350 =

3) Explain '20% of the beds in the new hospital are still empty'.

4) Sulphacetamide, used for treatment of corneal ulceration, comes in 10, 20 and 30% eye-drops and 2.5 and 6% eye ointment. Which preparation gives the strongest dose of sulphacetamide and which gives the weakest?

5) How much water is needed to make 100 ml of 15% dextrose solution?

6) What quantities of water and Dettol are needed to make 2 litres of 18% disinfectant?

Unit 5. Test on Indices

1) $2^3 =$

2) $3^2 =$

3) $2 \times 10^6 =$

4) Put the numbers 6^3, 2^3, 9^3, 4^3, 1^8 in order of size, largest first.

5) Put the numbers below in order of size, largest first.
   2.4×10^7, 5.9×10^5, 9.8×10^6, 4.4×10^5

6) Which of the following represent the same number?
   3^9, 9^3, 9000, 3×10^9, 9×10^3

Answers

Unit 1

1) 1500 g
   0.052 kg

2) 0.00456 mg
   720 micrograms

3) 0.18 m
   7600 mm

4) 0.075 ml
   20 000 μl

5) 1 000 000 units
   4.184 kJ

6) Mg, kg, g, mg, μg

Unit 2

1) 2½ pills
2) Use ½ an ampoule and discard the rest
3) 0.25 ml
4) 0.3 ml
5) 5 ml
6) 2 ml

Unit 3

1) 38 mpg
2) c = 24
3) 615 ml per day
4) ⅔ or 0.67 ml
5) 52 pills
6) 4.3 kg

Unit 4

1) $\frac{5}{100}$ or 0.05
2) 7
3) Out of every hundred beds, 20 are empty and 80 have patients in them
4) 30% eye-drops are strongest; 2.5% eye ointment is weakest
5) 85 ml
6) 0.36 l (or 360 ml) Dettol and 1.64 l (or 1640 ml) water

Unit 5

1) 8
2) 9
3) 2 000 000
4) 9^3, 6^3, 4^3, 2^3, 1^8
5) 2.4×10^7, 9.8×10^6, 5.9×10^5, 4.4×10^5
6) 9000 and 9×10^3 are the same

UNIT 1

SI Units

On 1st December 1975 the National Health Service in the UK adopted the International System of Units (Système International d'Unités or SI units) and abandoned all other measurement units. Contrary to what you may feel SI units were suggested as an international unit system in order to make it **easier** and **safer** for countries to communicate with each other.

Unfortunately for the British, we were one of the countries with the 'odd' units which the SI units were designed to eliminate. In fact we were in a real muddle internally since we were already using imperial units, apothecaries' units and some metric units.

Take a deep breath—forget anything you know about metric units—and turn over.

Once you have got the hang of how they work SI units are **simple**.

The basic idea behind SI units is a simple one. There is one base unit for each measurement (length, weight, etc.).

For example: the base unit for length is 'metre'. This can be abbreviated to 'm'. Be careful—the abbreviation is a small 'm', **not** a capital 'M'. This is very important, as you will see later.

To write eight metres in its short form we put 8 m.

Check 1

Why were SI units introduced?

What is the base SI unit for length?

How is this unit abbreviated?

Write 'seven base units of length' in a shorter way.

Other units from the SI system are:

Weight: gram shortened to g
Liquid volume: litre shortened to l

Notice again that capital letters are not used to represent litres and grams.

Thus, two litres can be written as 2 l and seven grams can be written as 7 g

Check 2

Write in words:

3 l

9 g

12 m

There are three further units which a nurse needs to know, and which you may not have met before. They are:

1. Mole: base unit of molecular weight shortened to mol
2. Joule: base unit of energy (used instead of calories) shortened to J
3. Pascal: base unit of pressure shortened to Pa

Notice that the shortened form of joule and pascal is a capital letter. You will remember this more easily if you realise that these units are named after Dr J.P. Joule, an English physicist in the 19th century, and Blaise Pascal, a French mathematician and physicist of the 17th century.

Possibly very few nursing learners have a useful understanding of molecular weights, so a very brief explanation is called for. (You will always find a fact easier to memorise if you have a peg to hang it on, i.e. if you can relate it to some other piece of knowledge. A French poem is much easier to learn by heart if you understand French.)

Many substances have a known molecular weight, e.g. the molecular weight of sodium is 23. (You are **not** expected to know these figures.)

From this a mole of sodium is defined as being 23 grams.

Given the molecular weight of dextrose as 180, we know that a mole of dextrose is 180 g.

Given the molecular weight of chlorine as 35.5, we know that one mole of chlorine is 35.5 g.

You will meet this unit in pathology laboratory reports and in concentrations in solutions.

Check 3

What is the base unit of pressure?

What is the base unit of energy?

What is the base unit of molecular weight?

Write in full:

   17 J

   8 mol

   4 Pa

Write in shortened form:

   eight litres

   twenty five metres

   one hundred and six grams

Any measurement can be written quite correctly using only the base units but strings of noughts can lead to mistakes.

You may write 300000 g. But can you tell at a glance whether it is three hundred thousand or three million grams?

Once again the SI units provide a simple solution.

For any unit we have the following rules:

One thousand units is called a kilo unit.

One thousand kilo units (i.e. a million units) is called a Mega unit. (Notice the capital M, although the unit was not invented by Mr Megaman!)

So that:

> One thousand metres is one kilometre and is written as 1 km.
>
> Thirteen thousand litres is thirteen kilolitres and is written as 13 kl.
>
> Two thousand kilolitres is two Megalitres and is written as 2 Ml.
>
> Sixty five million grams is sixty five Megagrams and is written as 65 Mg.

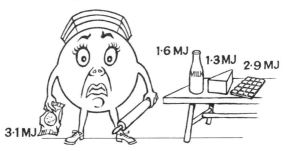

Check 4

What is a kilo unit?

What is a Mega unit?

Given that 1 kg means 1 kilogram = one thousand grams. Fill in the gaps:

8 km	means	=
497 MJ	means	=
15 kPa	means	=

Rewrite in appropriate units as in the first example:

$$
\begin{array}{rcl}
1\,000 \text{ m} &=& 1 \text{ km} \\
5\,000 \text{ l} &=& \\
25\,000\,000 \text{ g} &=& \\
1\,000 \text{ mol} &=& \\
176\,000 \text{ kPa} &=& \\
27\,000\,000 \text{ J} &=& \\
20\,000 \text{ km} &=& \\
\end{array}
$$

TAKE A BREAK NOW

Just as very large numbers (90000000 g) of base units are difficult to read and increase the risk of error, so are very small numbers. Consider 0.000006 l. At a glance are there six zeros after the decimal point or five?

SI units eliminate this problem.

A quick piece of revision:

  0.1 means one tenth
  0.01 means one hundredth
  0.001 means one thousandth
  0.000 1 means one ten-thousandth
  0.000 01 means one hundred-thousandth
  0.000 001 means one millionth

For any unit we have the following rules:

  One thousandth of a unit is called a milli unit.

  One thousandth of a milli unit (i.e. a millionth of a unit) is called a micro unit.

Thus we can say:

  One thousandth of a metre is a millimetre and is written as mm
  Six thousandths of a litre is 6 millilitres and is written as 6 ml
  Five thousandths of a milligram is 5 micrograms and is written as 5 micrograms★★
  0.007 l is 7 millilitres and is written as 7 ml
  0.000 026 m is 26 micrometres and is written as 26 micrometres★★
  0.009 mm (0.009 millimetres) is 9 micrometres

**VERY IMPORTANT

The classic short form for micro is μ (pronounced mew). This symbol is used in printed and typed documents and sometimes by doctors. **Never** use μ when writing micro units because it is very easily confused with the letter 'm', giving a unit ONE THOUSAND TIMES TOO LARGE! Always write in full 'micro unit'.

(Remember the mole? In fact you will most often meet this unit as 'millimole per litre', giving the concentration of some substance in a solution. This compound unit is abbreviated to mmol/l.)

Check 5

What is a thousandth of a unit called?

What is a millionth of a unit called?

What does μ stand for?

Given that 4 mg means 4 milligrams = four thousandths of a gram. Fill in the gaps:

6 mm means   =

2 μg means   =

7 mmol means   =

There is one further form of writing the units which you will meet. Drug doses are frequently written in the form '0.25 ml'. This should not worry you. Just remember one milli unit is 1000 micro units.

So 0.25 ml   = 0.25 × 1000 microlitres
                           = 250 microlitres

Also, 1.375 km   = 1.375 × 1000 m
                           = 1375 m

In reverse:

  2750 micrograms   = 2750 ÷ 1000 milligrams
                           = 2.75 mg (or 2.750 mg)

  4765 kJ   = 4765 ÷ 1000 MJ
                           = 4.765 MJ

One thousand, 1000, is the factor you need to remember when changing from one unit to a larger or smaller one.

In an attempt to avoid the danger inherent in changing from one unit to another the BNF (British National Formulary) have instituted a rule that all small doses should be prescribed in micrograms, not as decimal parts of a milligram. Eventually this may become established practice and your life will be easier—meanwhile you need to **beware**!

Check 6

Fill in the following:

460 micrometres	=	mm
1.675 kJ	=	J
0.2 mol	=	mmol
250 kPa	=	Pa

Now you have learnt the basis of all you need to know about SI Units.

Summary

Weight:	gram	(g)
Length:	metre	(m)
Liquid volume:	litre	(l)
Energy:	joule	(J)
Pressure:	pascal	(Pa)
Molecular weight:	mole	(mol)

The SI units consist of a single unit, two larger units and two smaller units for each measurement which will concern a nurse. For example:

Megalitre	kilolitre	litre	millilitre	microlitre
Ml	kl	l	ml	microlitre
Thousand kl	Thousand l	l	thousandth of l	thousandth of ml

To convert from one unit to another, remember this diagram:

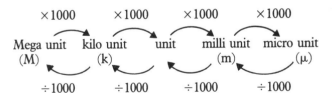

Now look back through the unit to refresh your memory and then turn over for the final check test.

Final check

Place in order of size, starting with the largest: microgram, gram, Megagram, milligram, kilogram.

Given that g stands for gram, a unit of weight, fill in the gaps:

l stands for	a unit of
kPa stands for	a unit of
μm stands for	a unit of
mmol stands for	a unit of
MJ stands for	a unit of

Fill in the following:

12 km	=	m
0.725 mg	=	μg
5375 kJ	=	MJ
2.65 kPa	=	Pa
4.2 l	=	ml
0.065 mol/l	=	mmol/l

Answers

Check 1

SI units were introduced to make international communication of measurements safer and simpler.
the metre
m
7 m

Check 2

Three litres
Nine grams
Twelve metres

Check 3

the pascal
the joule
the mole

Seventeen joules
Eight moles
Four pascals

8 l
25 m
106 g

Check 4

One thousand units
One thousand kilo units or one million units

8 kilometres = 8 thousand metres (8000 m)
497 Megajoules = 497 thousand kilojoules (497 000 kJ) or 497 million joules (497 000 000 J)
15 kilopascals = 15 thousand pascals (15 000 Pa)

5 kl
25 Mg
1 kmol
176 MPa
27 MJ
20 Mm

Check 5

Milli unit
Micro unit
Micro

6 millimetres	= 6 thousandths of a metre
2 micrograms	= 2 thousandths of a milligram
	= 2 millionths of a gram
7 millimoles	= 7 thousandths of a mole

Check 6

0.46(0) (last zero is not strictly necessary, but it is also not wrong)
1675 J
200 mmol
250 000 Pa

Final check

Mg, kg, g, mg, μg
litre — liquid volume
kilopascal — pressure
micrometre — length
millimole — molecular weight
Megajoule — energy

12 000 m
725 micrograms
5.375 MJ
2650 Pa
4200 ml
65 mmol/l

Drug Doses

Giving patients medicine is one part of a nurse's work which everyone knows about. Most people, too, are well aware of the dangers of overdoses. Tragic mistakes resulting in death are given wide coverage by the press and these mistakes are usually mathematical mistakes. Every nurse needs to be 100% accurate every time a dose of medicine is given.

Fortunately, calculating drug doses can be simple, as you will see.

You may well meet, or even have already met, several different ways of calculating a drug dose. Books and tutors use various formulae, all of which eventually produce the right answer for the drug being administered.

In this book you will learn that there is one, very simple formula which will always work.

Why is there any problem at all since it is the doctor who prescribes the dose that a patient will be given? Surely all the nurse has to do is just give it? The problem is that the medicament prescribed by a doctor may not be packaged in the precise dose which he wants to administer.

Consider a simple example. The doctor prescribes a dose of 8 mg of nicoumalone (an anticoagulant) for a patient being treated for thrombosis. This drug is supplied in 4 mg tablets. The nurse must therefore work out how many tablets the patient should be given: 2 tablets—easy!

Stop and think how you worked that out:

The dose prescribed was 8 mg
The dose per pill was 4 mg

So the number of pills to be given $= \dfrac{\text{Dose prescribed}}{\text{Dose per pill}}$

$$= \frac{8}{4}$$

$$= 2$$

Look at another example:

The doctor prescribes 75 mg of amitriptyline for a patient suffering from depression.

Amitriptyline comes in 25 mg pills.

Dose prescribed = 75 mg
Dose per pill = 25 mg

So the number of pills $= \dfrac{\text{Dose prescribed}}{\text{Dose per pill}} = \dfrac{75}{25} = 3$

Accuracy in drug administration is vital. Mistakes are easily made. **Always look at the result of your calculations and think 'Is that a sensible answer?'**

Look at the examples on this page. Even though you are not familiar with the particular drugs being used you can consider 2 or 3 pills as a reasonable dose. Eight or 10 would not be a reasonable dose so you would need to re-check your working.

Check 1

An analgesic is prescribed for a woman in a single dose of 50 mg. The capsules contain 25 mg of the drug each. How many capsules should she be given?

Aspirin is dispensed in 300 mg pills. How many pills are needed for a dose of 900 mg? How many pills are needed each day for a dose of 600 mg, three times a day?

The dose of 150 mg of aspirin is recommended for a five-year-old child. How many pills should be given?

Penicillin is dispensed in 250 mg pills. How many pills are needed to give a child a dose of 125 mg?

So now we have a formula which copes with pills. What about liquid medicines?

A doctor prescribes 10 mg of codeine as a cough suppressant. Codeine is dispensed as 5 mg of codeine per teaspoonful of linctus.

Dose prescribed   = 10 mg
Dose per spoonful =   5 mg

So the patient will need 2 teaspoonfuls of linctus.

Is this a reasonable answer? Yes, 2 teaspoonfuls is a quantity acceptable to a patient.

How did we work that out? Is there a formula being used here like the pill formula?

Yes. Number of teaspoonfuls $= \dfrac{\text{Dose prescribed}}{\text{Dose per teaspoonful}}$

$$= \frac{10}{5}$$

Key sequence

$\boxed{\text{off}}$ $\boxed{\text{on}}$ $\boxed{1}$ $\boxed{0}$ $\boxed{\div}$ $\boxed{5}$ $\boxed{=}$

$$= 2$$

Example

A doctor prescribes 25 mg of a drug to be given by injection. It is a drug dispensed in a solution of strength 50 mg per ml.
How many ml should the nurse give?

Dose prescribed   = 25 mg
Dose per ml   = 50 mg

$$\text{Number of ml to be given} = \frac{\text{Dose prescribed}}{\text{Dose per ml}}$$

$$= \frac{25}{50}$$

$$= 0.5$$

Key sequence

| off | on | 2 | 5 | ÷ | 5 | 0 | = |

Reasonable answer? Yes, 0.5 ml is a common volume to inject.

How can you check whether your calculation has been correct?

Medicines are manufactured and packed in a form which will make a dose both palatable to the patient (e.g. not more than 3 or 4 spoonfuls) and easy to administer by the nurse (e.g. not in such concentrated form that the nurse needs to give ⅕ of a pill). All drugs are now dispensed in metric quantities, most commonly mg and ml. The 'teaspoonful' has been replaced by the '5-ml medicine spoon' which is a little larger.

Hints to remember, therefore, when checking your calculations (even for unfamiliar drugs) are:

1) 15–20 ml (3 or 4 medicine spoonfuls) are likely to be the maximum dose of a liquid medicament.
2) 3 or 4 pills or capsules are likely to be the maximum dose of solid medicaments.
3) Injection quantities normally range between 0.25 ml and 2 ml.
4) A child's dose is almost always less than the adult standard dose. (The result '½ an aspirin' was a reasonable answer for the dose for a child in Check 1.)

As you become more experienced you will remember the normal quantities prescribed for the drugs in common use and this will obviously make it easy to check your dose calculations.

But familiar or unfamiliar, you must **always check** your answers for 'unreasonableness'.

Check 2

Papaveretum (an injection containing opium) comes in an ampoule containing 20 mg in 1 ml.

How many ml should be injected if 10 mg are prescribed?

How many ml should be injected if 15 mg are prescribed?

Comment on your answers.

Digoxin is a drug used in connection with the heart. A stock bottle contains elixir with 0.05 mg per ml. If the prescription is 0.5 mg, how much elixir should be given?

A nurse reads a prescription for 2.5 mg of digoxin. How much elixir should she give?

Comment on your answers.

The stock bottle of sulphadimidine, used to arrest the growth of bacteria, contains 100 mg per ml. The prescription reads 3000 mg as an initial dose. How many ml should be given orally?

A nurse takes the stock bottle of ampicilin, 25 g per ml, to give an oral dose of 0.5 g. How many ml should be given?

Comment on your answers.

So far we have three formulae for drug calculations:

1. Number of pills $\quad = \dfrac{\text{Dose prescribed}}{\text{Dose per pill}}$

2. Number of teaspoonfuls $= \dfrac{\text{Dose prescribed}}{\text{Dose per teaspoonful}}$

3. Number of ml $\quad = \dfrac{\text{Dose prescribed}}{\text{Dose per ml}}$

But you were promised **one** formula which always works! We can in fact make a general formula which does cover all these separate cases. Consider:

Number of 'measures' to be given $= \dfrac{\text{Dose prescribed}}{\text{Dose per 'measure'}}$

If the 'measure' is a pill we have formula 1
If the 'measure' is a millilitre we have formula 3, and so on . . .

However, a 'measure' does not always need to be pills, spoonfuls or ml.

Problem

A patient needs 160 calories. A boiled egg contains 80 calories. How many eggs should he have for breakfast? It is the 'How much . . .' or 'How many . . .' part of the problem which gives you what your 'measure' is.
So if we say the 'measure' is an egg, we have:

Number of eggs $= \dfrac{\text{Dose prescribed}}{\text{Dose per egg}} = \dfrac{160}{80} = 2$

(Correct!)

Learn this formula

Number of 'measures' to be given $= \dfrac{\text{Dose prescribed}}{\text{Dose per 'measure'}}$

Check 3

What is the drug formula which must be indelibly written on your heart?

Having done your calculation from the formula, what next?

⊤⒜⒦⒠ ⒜ ⒝⒭⒠⒜⒦ ⒩⒪⒲

In all the examples we have looked at, the units for the dose prescribed and for the dose per 'measure' have been the same. For example, the doctor has prescribed 75 **mg** of amitriptyline and it comes in 25 **mg** pills or the doctor has prescribed 10 **mg** of codeine and this is dispensed as 5 **mg** per teaspoon.

What happens if the doctor prescribes an injection of 200 micrograms of drug and the stock bottle contains 1 milligram per ml? Here the dose prescribed is in micrograms and the dose per 'measure' is in milligrams.

Before you use the golden formula you must make sure that the two dose values are in the same units. If they are not, as in this case, you must convert the dose prescribed to the same units as the dose per 'measure'.★

Here we have:

'Dose per measure' unit = **mg** (1 mg per ml)
Dose prescribed = 200 μg = 0.2 **mg**

The formula then gives:
Number of 'measures' (ml) to be given $= \dfrac{0.2}{1} = 0.2$

The injection is 0.2 ml, which is reasonable!

★ Strictly speaking, it does not matter what units you use as long as they are the same for both dose values. **But** the arithmetic is **always easier** if you convert to the units of the dose per 'measure'.

Example

A doctor prescribes 0.5 g of aspirin which is dispensed in 250 mg pills. How many pills are needed?

The formula is:

$$\text{Number of 'measures' to be given} = \frac{\text{Dose prescribed}}{\text{Dose per 'measure'}}$$

The 'measure' is pill
The 'dose per measure' unit is **mg** (250 mg per pill)
The dose prescribed = 0.5 g = 500 **mg**

So the number of pills to be given $= \dfrac{500}{250} = 2$

The patient should be given 2 pills. This is reasonable.

Example

A doctor prescribes 500 mg of a drug, by injection. The stock bottle label says 'solution 1 g per ml'. How many ml should be given?

The formula is:

$$\text{Number of 'measures' to be given} = \frac{\text{Dose prescribed}}{\text{Dose per 'measure'}}$$

The 'measure' is ml
The 'dose per measure' unit = **g** (1 g per ml)
The dose prescribed = 500 mg = 0.5 **g**
So the number of ml to be given $= \dfrac{0.5}{1} = 0.5$

The nurse gives 0.5 ml by injection, which is OK.

To solve *any* drug problem you meet in the whole of your career as a nurse you need to remember two things:
1. The 'golden' formula:

Number of 'measures' to be given =

$$\frac{\text{Dose prescribed}}{\text{Dose per 'measure'}}$$

---

2. The order of calculation:

(a) Decide what your 'measure' is.
(b) If necessary change 'dose prescribed' units to be the same as the 'dose per measure' units.
(c) Use the formula to calculate the quantity of medicament needed.
(d) Check the 'reasonableness' of your answer.

Example

A mug holds 125 ml of water. A patient must drink 0.5 litres. How many mugs of water must be drunk?

(a) The 'measure' is mug
(b) The 'dose per measure' unit = ml (125 ml per mug)
   The dose prescribed = 0.5 litre = 500 ml
(c) So the number of 'measures' to be drunk

$$= \frac{\text{Dose prescribed}}{\text{Dose per 'measure' (mug)}}$$

$$= \frac{500}{125}$$

Key sequence

| off | on | 5 | 0 | 0 | ÷ | 1 | 2 | 5 | = |

$$= 4$$

(d) The patient must drink 4 mugs of water, which is quite possible.

Check 4

What is the golden formula?

How many stages are there in a drug calculation?

What are the stages?

A doctor prescribes 1.5 g of sulphadimidine, which is in a solution of 100 mg per ml. How many ml of the stock solution should be given orally?

So far we have only looked at situations where the stock medicament is known as so many mg 'per ml' or 'per pill'.

Problem

A doctor prescribes 200 mg of ampicillin. The stock bottle is labelled 125 mg **per 5 ml**. How many ml must be given?

Think of the four steps of drug administration:

(a) Decide on 'measure' (in this case it is ml)
(b) 'Dose per measure' unit is **mg** (125 mg per 5 ml)
     Dose prescribed = 200 **mg**. Units match, so OK
(c) Use the formula:

Number of 'measures' (ml) to be given =

$$\frac{\text{Dose prescribed}}{\text{Dose per 'measure'}}$$

Dose prescribed = 200 mg
Dose per ml   = ?

The stock solution is '125 mg per 5 ml', so before we can use the formula we need to calculate 'dose per ml':

5 ml contains 125 mg

so 1 ml contains $\dfrac{125}{5}$ = 25 mg

i.e. dose per 'measure' = 25 mg

Therefore number of ml to be given = $\dfrac{200}{25}$ = 8

(d) The nurse must give 8 ml of oral ampicillin and this is a reasonable answer.

Example

Trimeprazine, an oral premedication, is available in stock strength 30 mg per 5 ml. The prescription is 24 mg.

(a) The 'measure' is ml
(b) 'Dose per measure' unit is **mg** (30 mg per 5 ml)
    Dose prescribed = 24 **mg**. OK
(c) Using this formula:

Number of 'measures' (ml) to be given =

$$\frac{\text{Dose prescribed}}{\text{Dose per 'measure' (ml)}}$$

Dose prescribed = 24 mg
Dose per ml   = ?

    5 ml contains 30 mg

so 1 ml contains $\dfrac{30}{5}$ = 6 mg

i.e. dose per ml = 6 mg

Number of ml to be given = $\dfrac{24}{6}$ = 4

(d) The nurse must give 4 ml of trimeprazine. This sounds OK.

The arithmetic coming out of the formula has been pretty simple up to now. Before you go on through the unit you might like to practise a little with your calculator.

Check 5

1) $\dfrac{27}{0.3} =$

2) $\dfrac{7.25}{0.2} =$

3) $\dfrac{170}{8.5} =$

4) $\dfrac{1.25}{4} =$

5) $\dfrac{13.2}{0.6} =$

6) $\dfrac{0.006}{0.12} =$

Going back to the drug calculations, here are a few more examples.

Example 1

Digoxin is available as an elixir, 0.1 mg per 2 ml. The prescription is for 250 µg.

(a) The 'measure' is ml
(b) 'Dose per measure' unit is **mg** (0.1 mg per 2 ml)
    Dose prescribed = 250 µg = 0.25 **mg**
(c) Using the formula:

Number of 'measures' (ml) to be given =

$$\frac{\text{Dose prescribed}}{\text{Dose per 'measure' (ml)}}$$

Dose prescribed = 0.25 mg
Dose per ml = ?

In stock solution   2 ml contains 0.1 mg

so 1 ml contains $\dfrac{0.1}{2}$ = 0.05 mg

i.e. dose per ml = 0.05 mg

Number of ml to be given = $\dfrac{0.25}{0.05}$ = 5

(d) The nurse must give 5 ml and this is a reasonable answer (i.e. one medicine spoonful).

Example 2

Atropine (a premedication by injection) is in stock strength of 3 mg per 5 ml. Prescription is 0.15 mg for a child going to theatre.

(a) The 'measure' is ml
(b) 'Dose per measure' unit is **mg** (3 mg per 5 ml)
    Dose prescribed = 0.15 **mg**. OK
(c) Using the formula:

Number of 'measures' (ml) to be given =

$$\frac{\text{Dose prescribed}}{\text{Dose per 'measure' (ml)}}$$

Dose prescribed = 0.15 mg
Dose per ml = ?

5 ml contains 3 mg

so 1 ml contains $\dfrac{3}{5}$ = 0.6 mg

i.e. dose per ml = 0.6 mg

Number of ml to be given = $\dfrac{0.15}{0.6}$ = 0.25

(d) The nurse must give 0.25 ml which sounds reasonable for a child's injection.

Example 3

Pethidine is dispensed in ampoules containing 100 mg of drug in 2 ml. How many ampoules does the nurse need to get in order to give 25 mg of pethidine to a child?

(a) What is a 'measure' here? Since the nurse wants to know how many ampoules are needed, take one ampoule as the 'measure'.

(b) 'Dose per measure' unit is **mg** (100 mg per ampoule) Dose prescribed = 25 **mg**. OK

(c) Using the formula:

Number of 'measures' (ampoules) to be used =

$$\frac{\text{Dose prescribed}}{\text{Dose per 'measure' (ampoule)}}$$

Dose prescribed = 25 mg

Dose per ampoule = 100 mg

Notice that since we are taking an ampoule as our 'measure' we are not concerned with the 2 ml. Each ampoule contains 100 mg of pethidine.

Number of ampoules = $\frac{25}{100}$ = 0.25 or ¼

The nurse needs to use ¼ of an ampoule for the child

(d) ¼ of an ampoule seems reasonable since it is less than a whole ampoule which is probably packaged to be a standard adult dose. (Incidentally the rest of the ampoule would be thrown away.)

Example 4

Consider Example 3 when we wish to know how many ml the child should have

(a) This time the 'measure' is ml

(b) 'Dose per measure' unit is **mg** (100 mg per 2 ml)
Dose prescribed = 25 **mg**. OK

(c) Using the formula:

Number of 'measures' (ml) to be given =

$$\frac{\text{Dose prescribed}}{\text{Dose per 'measure' (ml)}}$$

Dose prescribed = 25 mg

Dose per ml = ?

2 ml contains 100 mg
so 1 ml contains 50 mg

Number of ml given = $\frac{25}{50}$ = 0.5

The nurse must give 0.5 ml to the child

(d) The whole ampoule holds 2 ml and a quarter of this is 0.5 ml, so the answer agrees with what we calculated in Example 3.

Check 6

Find the quantity of medicament to be given in each of the following examples.

1) 500 mg of drug per 2 ml elixir. Prescription 250 mg, orally.
2) 0.05 mg of drug per ml. Prescription 0.3 mg, orally.
3) 0.3 mg of drug per 5 ml. Prescription for a child 0.012 mg, intravenously.
4) 5 mg of drug per capsule. Prescription 30 mg.
5) 250 mg of drug per 2 ml. Prescription 15 mg orally.

TAKE A BREAK NOW

There is one drug which is worth examining briefly on its own: heparin. This is an anticoagulant given to prevent or lower the risk of blood clotting within the body. It acts rapidly but is also quickly eliminated from the system. This leads to doses of very different sizes being required by different patients or even by the same patient during a course of treatment.

Heparin is usually given either by intravenous injection every 6 hours, the dose being regulated by pathology reports on prothrombin times, or, diluted with sodium chloride, via a heparin pump, often over 24 hours.

The available strengths of heparin are as follows:

1 000 international units (i.u.) per ml in a 5 ml vial
5 000 i.u. per ml in a 5 ml vial
25 000 i.u. per ml in a 5 ml vial
100 i.u. per ml in a 2 ml vial

You will never need to do calculations involving heparin packaged as 100 i.u. since this small dose is merely used to flush the needle and keep the path of intravenous injection open.

Example

A doctor prescribes 10 000 i.u. to be injected intravenously. Before you can calculate the dose to be given you need to decide which strength to use.

First consider 1000 i.u. per ml.

Follow the four stages as before.

(a) The 'measure' is ml
(b) 'Dose per measure' is in i.u. (1000 i.u. per ml)
     Dose prescribed = 10 000 i.u. OK
(c) Using the formula:

Number of 'measures' (ml) to be given

$$= \frac{\text{Dose prescribed}}{\text{Dose per 'measure'}}$$
$$= \frac{10\,000}{1\,000}$$
$$= 10$$

(d) 10 ml is far too much for an injection.

So, now consider 5000 i.u. per ml.

(a) The 'measure' is ml

(b) 'Dose per measure' is in i.u. (5000 i.u. per ml)
Dose prescribed is also in i.u.

(c) Number of ml to be given $= \dfrac{10\,000}{5\,000}$

$\qquad\qquad\qquad\qquad\qquad\quad = 2$

(d) 2 ml is a possible injection quantity.

But also consider 25 000 units per ml.

(a) The 'measure' is ml

(b) 'Dose per measure' is in i.u. (25 000 i.u. per ml)
Dose prescribed is also in i.u.

(c) Number of ml to be given $= \dfrac{10\,000}{25\,000}$

$\qquad\qquad\qquad\qquad\qquad\quad = 0.4$

(d) 0.4 ml is definitely preferable as an injection since it
is the smallest quantity available here.

Most heparin comes in multi-dose containers (vials)
rather than ampoules and these contain a preservative
which enables any unused drug to be kept for future use
rather than being thrown away immediately.

Example

A patient is prescribed 1500 i.u. per hour to be given in a saline infusion.
Consider the three possible strengths:

    1000 i.u./ml   5000 i.u./ml   25 000 i.u./ml

For each of the strengths follow the four stages.

(a) The 'measure' is ml
(b) 'Dose per measure' is in i.u.
     Dose prescribed is also in i.u.
(c) Using the formula:

Number of measures (ml) to be given

$$= \frac{\text{Dose prescribed}}{\text{Dose per 'measure'}}$$

$$= \frac{1500}{1000} \quad \text{or} = \frac{1500}{5000} \quad \text{or} = \frac{1500}{25\,000}$$

$$= 1.5 \quad \text{or} = 0.3 \quad \text{or} = 0.06$$

(d) 1.5 ml of 1000 strength is OK.
     0.3 ml of 5000 strength is OK.
     0.06 ml of 25 000 strength is too small to measure accurately. If heparin is not being given as an injection directly to the patient but is being added to a saline infusion, it is not necessary to always take the smallest quantity. Here, either 1.5 ml of 1000 i.u./ml or 0.3 ml of 5000 i.u./ml will do.

Remember, too, that error when measuring a very concentrated form of drug, such as 25 000 i.u. per ml is more dangerous than with less concentrated drugs.

There are a few other drugs which also come in a variety of strengths. When the strength to use is not prescribed you will have to calculate the dose to be given for each strength and decide which is the most appropriate quantity to give.

Example

The stock cupboard contains morphine sulphate in strengths 10 mg/ml and 20 mg/ml. Which would you use to inject a prescribed dose of 15 mg?

Consider 10 mg/ml

(a) The 'measure' is ml
(b) 'Dose per measure' is in mg
    Dose prescribed is also in mg

(c) Using the formula: $\dfrac{15}{10} = 1.5$

(d) Inject 1.5 ml. This is OK.

Consider 20 mg/ml

(a) The 'measure' is ml
(b) 'Dose per measure' is in mg
    Dose prescribed is also in mg

(c) Using the formula: $\dfrac{15}{20} = 0.75$

(d) Inject 0.75 ml. This is better because it is less.

Check 7

1. Heparin is available in three strengths:

> 1 000 i.u. per ml
> 5 000 i.u. per ml
> 25 000 i.u. per ml

Calculate the most appropriate quantity to use for the following prescriptions:

(a)   8 000 i.u. by intravenous injection
(b)   2 000 i.u. in a saline infusion over 2 hours
(c) 40 000 i.u. in a saline infusion over 24 hours

2. A drug is available in the following strengths:

> 10 mg/ml   20 mg/ml   40 mg/ml

Which strength would you use for an injection of:

(a) 25 mg
(b)   8 mg
(c) 30 mg

You have now learned the vital formula and understand how to use it. If you always follow the four stages of the calculation routine, you will be a safe and competent nurse when handling drugs.

Summary

1. Vital, all-weather formula:

   Number of 'measures' to be given =

   $$\frac{\text{Dose prescribed}}{\text{Dose per 'measure'}}$$

2. Calculation routine:

   (a) Decide what is the 'measure' (e.g. ml or pill or ...)

   (b) If necessary change the 'dose prescribed' units so that they are the same as the 'dose per measure' units.

   (c) Use the formula. You may need to calculate the dose per 'measure' if the stock strength is not as you would like it to be.

   (d) Is your answer reasonable?
   Rough guide:

   Oral doses: 1 ml to 20 ml
   Pills: 1 to 4 pills
   Injections: 0.25 ml to 2 ml
   Child's dose: less than adult's dose

Final check

Find the quantity of medicament to be given in each of the examples 1–12.

1) Penicillin: 125 mg per tablet. Dose prescribed: 375 mg for adult.
2) Pethidine: 50 mg per ml. Dose prescribed: 75 mg orally.
3) Papaveretum: 20 mg in 1 ml ampoules. Dose prescribed: 15 mg as an injection.
4) Atropine: 3 mg per 5 ml. Dose prescribed: 0.27 mg as an injection.
5) Anysiciline: 500 mg in 2 ml. Dose prescribed: 1 g orally.
6) Digoxin: 0.1 mg in 2 ml. Dose prescribed: 1 mg intravenously.
7) Digoxin (Paediatric): 0.1 mg in 2 ml elixir. Dose prescribed: 0.5 mg orally for a one-year-old child.
8) Pirmecillinam (for typhoid): 200 mg per tablet. Dose prescribed: 2.4 g daily.
9) Sulphadimidine: 500 mg in 5 ml. Dose prescribed: 1.5 g.
10) Morphine sulphate comes in ampoules of various strengths: 10 mg/ml, 15 mg/ml, 20 mg/ml and 30 mg/ml. An injection of 8 mg is prescribed. Which strength and how much of it would you use?
11) Now consider similarly a prescription for an injection of 27 mg of morphine sulphate.
12) A doctor prescribes 9000 i.u. of heparin by intravenous injection. 1000 i.u./ml, 5000 i.u./ml and 25 000 i.u./ml are all available. Which strength and how much of it would you give the patient?

Answers

Check 1

2 capsules

3 pills
6 pills
½ pill

½ pill

Check 2

0.5 ml (or ½ ml)	Reasonable injection
0.75 ml (or ¾ ml)	Reasonable injection
10 ml	Reasonable oral dose
50 ml	The nurse has probably mis-read the prescription and should check her dose with another nurse. Occasionally a single large dose of digoxin (a heart stimulant) is given in an emergency.
30 ml	This sounds a little large, although, as with digoxin, a single initial large dose may be prescribed.
0.02 ml	This is totally unreasonable as an oral dose. The nurse has probably mis-read the stock bottle (0.25 g?).

Check 3

$$\text{Number of 'measures' to be given} = \frac{\text{Dose prescribed}}{\text{Dose per 'measure'}}$$

Now check your calculated answer for 'reasonableness'.

Check 4

Number of 'measures' to be given = $\dfrac{\text{Dose prescribed}}{\text{Dose per 'measure'}}$

There are 4 stages.

(a)   Decide what is the 'measure'.
(b)   If necessary change the 'dose prescribed' units so that they are the same as the 'dose per measure' units.
(c)   Use the formula, calculating the 'dose per measure', if the stock strength is not as you would like it.
(d)   Check for 'reasonableness'.

15 ml. This will be 3 spoonfuls and is OK.

Check 5

1) 90
2) 36.25
3) 20
4) 0.3125
5) 22
6) 0.05

Check 6

1) 1 ml	Reasonable oral dose
2) 6 ml	Reasonable oral dose
3) 0.2 ml	Reasonable as an injection
4) 6 capsules	This sounds a lot. Nurse should check the prescription and capsule contents again.
5) 0.12 ml	This is much too small to be given orally. The nurse should check her instructions and calculations again. **Did you**?

Check 7

1) (a)   8 ml of 1 000 i.u./ml Too much
              1.6 ml of 5 000 i.u./ml OK
              0.32 ml of 25 000 i.u./ml Hard to measure accurately

    (b)   2 ml of 1 000 i.u./ml OK
              0.4 ml of 5 000 i.u./ml OK
              0.08 ml of 25 000 i.u./ml Too small to be accurate

    (c)   40 ml of 1 000 i.u./ml Too much
              8 ml of 5 000 i.u./ml Too much
              1.6 ml of 25 000 i.u./ml OK

2) (a)   2.5 ml of 10 mg/ml Too much
              1.25 ml of 20 mg/ml OK
              0.625 ml of 40 mg/ml Hard to measure exactly

    (b)   0.8 ml of 10 mg/ml OK
              0.4 ml of 20 mg/ml OK
              0.2 ml of 40 mg/ml Rather small

    (c)   3.0 ml of 10 mg/ml Much too much
              1.5 ml of 20 mg/ml OK
              0.75 ml of 40 mg/ml OK. Best because it is the least

---

Final check

1) 3 tablets	OK for an adult
2) 1.5 ml	OK as an oral dose
3) 0.75 ml	OK as an injection
4) 0.45 ml	OK as an injection
5) 4 ml	OK as an oral dose
6) 20 ml	Sounds high but could be correct. Nurse must check.
7) 10 ml	Sounds very high for a 1-year-old child. Nurse must check.
8) 12 tablets daily	OK, probably prescribed as 3 tablets, 4 times a day.
9) 15 ml	OK as an oral dose, but not as an injection. Nurse should re-read prescription to find out how the drug is to be given.

10) 0.4 ml of 20 mg/ml strength is best. Strengths 15 mg/ml and 30 mg/ml cannot be used because it is not possible to measure accurately 0.53 (recurring) ml and 0.26 (recurring) ml respectively. 0.8 ml of 10 mg/ml strength is OK.

11) 2.7 ml of 10 mg/ml   Too much
    1.8 ml of 15 mg/ml   Just OK
    1.35 ml of 20 mg/ml   OK
    0.9 ml of 30 mg/ml   Best

12)   9 ml of 1 000 i.u./ml   Too much
     1.8 ml of 5 000 i.u./ml   OK
    0.36 ml of 25 000 i.u./ml   Hard to measure accurately
    So give 1.8 ml of 5000 i.u./ml

Formulae

A formula (plural is formulae or formulas) is a shorthand way of remembering how to do a calculation. You use them all the time without realising it.

A small tin of baked beans costs 10p. How much do five tins cost? 50p of course! But, in fact, you have used a formula to work the cost out:

Total cost (T) = cost of one tin (c) × number of tins (n)

or   T   = c × n

Most motorists are concerned about the quantity of petrol their cars use. They want to know how many mpg (miles per gallon) the car will do. To work this out they must divide the total number of miles driven (M) by the total quantity of petrol used (G):

$$\frac{\text{No. of miles driven}}{\text{No. of gallons of petrol used}} = \text{consumption rate (C)}$$

or $\frac{M}{G} = C$

Another example:

An 18-month-old baby is 1½ years old,

i.e. Age in years (A) $= \dfrac{\text{Age in months (a)}}{12}$

or $\qquad$ A $= \dfrac{a}{12}$

These examples may seem trivial, but that is because you are so familiar with them. Many of the nursing formulae will seem just as simple when you have worked through this unit.

Over the next few pages we will use the details of six particular babies when working with various formulae used in nursing babies and children. Below is some information taken from their record cards.

Name	Age	Weight (kg)	Birth weight (kg)	Recommended daily fluid intake (ml)	No. of meals per day
Robert	6 weeks	4.8	3.9	725	5
Sarah	4 weeks	3.8	3.2	575	6
Mary	6 weeks	4.7	3.5	725	4
Tom	1 month	5	4.4	750	6
Elizabeth	6 months	7	4.1		
Peter	3 weeks	1.75	1.8		

There are four stages involved in working with formulae:

---

1. Choose the right formula
2. Choose the right numbers to use
3. Put the numbers in the right places in the formula
4. Know how to use the answer.

Formulae can be written in two ways, either in word form

e.g. $\dfrac{\text{Distance in miles}}{\text{Gallons of petrol used}}$ = Consumption rate

or in algebraic form $\qquad \dfrac{M}{G} = C$

At this stage in your training you are **not** expected to know or remember any of the formulae used in this unit. The aim at this stage is to learn **how** to use formulae. If you remember the four stages then handling the formulae you will meet will be simple.

Check 1

How many stages are there to work through when using formulae?

What are they?

Babies, and particularly sick babies, must have their diet controlled to ensure that they get a sufficient amount of the correct foods each day. The number of feeds given to the baby each day may vary depending on hospital routine and the baby's sleeping pattern, age and weight!

A simple formula gives:

$$\text{Quantity at each feed} = \frac{\text{Recommended daily intake}}{\text{Number of feeds per day}}$$

From the record card (on page 84) we have

Sarah, 4 weeks, weight 3.8 kg, birth weight 3.2 kg, daily intake 575 ml, 6 feeds per day. How much should Sarah have at each feed?

1. The formula to use is the one just given above:

   $$\text{Quantity at each feed} = \frac{\text{Recommended daily intake}}{\text{Number of feeds per day}}$$

2. We need values for Sarah's recommended daily intake and for the number of feeds she is taking. From the record card we know that, daily intake = 575 ml and number of feeds = 6.

3. The formula gives us:

   $$\text{Quantity at each feed (ml)} = \frac{\text{Daily intake}}{\text{Number of feeds}}$$

   $$= \frac{575}{6} \text{ ml}$$

   Key sequence

   | off | on | 5 | 7 | 5 | ÷ | 6 | = |

   $$= 95.833333 \text{ ml}$$

4. The formula suggests that Sarah should have 95.83 ml per feed. There is no need to measure a feed to this degree of accuracy since you cannot measure the milk dribbled or spilt! Sarah should be given about 100 ml per feed. It is normal to estimate to the nearest 25 ml because it makes mixing the feed easier.

Robert. How much should Robert have at each feed?
(See page 84 for the record card details)

1. Using the formula:

   $$\text{Quantity at each feed} = \frac{\text{Recommended daily intake}}{\text{Number of feeds per day}}$$

2. The numbers needed are: daily intake = 725 ml;
   number of feeds = 5

3. Putting the numbers in the formula:

   $$\text{Quantity at each feed (ml)} = \frac{\text{Daily intake}}{\text{Number of feeds}}$$

   $$= \frac{725}{5} = 145 \text{ ml}$$

4. Robert needs about 150 ml per feed.

Check 2

Name	Age	Weight (kg)	Birth weight (kg)	Recommended daily fluid intake (ml)	Number of meals per day
Robert	6 weeks	4.8	3.9	725	5
Sarah	4 weeks	3.8	3.2	575	6
Mary	6 weeks	4.7	3.5	725	4
Tom	1 month	5	4.4	750	6
Elizabeth	6 months	7	4.1		
Peter	3 weeks	1.75	1.8		

How many millilitres do Tom and Mary need at each feed?

Comment on the difference between Robert's feed and that of Mary. (Robert needs 150 ml per feed.)

Usually a nurse has to calculate the recommended daily intake for a baby. There is a formula for doing this:

Daily fluid requirement (ml) = 150 × Body weight (kg)

Sarah

1. Using the formula: Daily fluid requirement in ml = 150 × Body weight in kg
2. The number needed is Sarah's weight, 3.8 kg
3. Fluid requirement = 150 × 3.8 = 570 ml
4. Sarah needs about 570 ml per feed, so 575, as given on her record card, is OK.

What about Mary?

1. Using the formula: Daily fluid requirement in ml = 150 × Body weight in kg
2. The number needed is Mary's weight, 4.7 kg
3. Fluid requirement = 150 × 4.7 = 705 ml
4. It is better to offer a little more feed that is essential because the baby may well spill some. Mary's daily fluid need is therefore about 725 ml.

Check 3

Name	Age	Weight (kg)	Birth weight (kg)	Recommended daily fluid intake (ml)	Number of meals per day
Robert	6 weeks	4.8	3.9	725	5
Sarah	4 weeks	3.8	3.2	575	6
Mary	6 weeks	4.7	3.5	725	4
Tom	1 month	5	4.4	750	6
Elizabeth	6 months	7	4.1		
Peter	3 weeks	1.75	1.8		

Calculate what you would expect Robert and Tom to be given each day in the way of fluids.

Use the formula:

Daily fluid requirement (ml) = 150 × Body weight (kg)

TAKE A BREAK NOW

When working with a formula, stage 2 (choosing the right numbers to use) requires a careful look. In the examples used on fluid requirement, the formula was

Daily fluid requirement in **ml** = 150 × Weight in **kg**

The National Health Service in the UK changed totally to using SI units on 1st December 1975, but many people still use pounds and pints.

You are not expected to be able to convert from imperial to SI units quickly in your head. You **must**, however, notice that the formula you are using needs SI units of measurement. There is a special danger here because, for speed and ease of remembering, the formula may be reduced to

Fluid needed = 150 × Weight

Tom, aged one month, weighs 11 lbs (5 kg on his record card). To give him 150 × 11 = 1650 ml (mixing imperial and SI!) would be grossly over-feeding him. 1650 pints is clearly nonsense too!

You are not likely to make this mistake if you stop and think what the answer is, i.e. a quantity of feed not just a numerical answer to a calculation. Even so you must watch the units you use because there will be times (e.g. when using unfamiliar drugs) when you may not know what size of answer to expect.

More complicated formulae

Sometimes a formula contains several operations e.g. addition, multiplication and some brackets. The rule for the order of working things out is:

*B*rackets
*O*f
*D*ivide
*M*ultiply
*A*dd
*S*ubtract

Remember this with the word ‘B   O   D   M   A   S’
                               () of ÷   ×   +   −

Your calculator, however, does not obey the BODMAS rule, it does each calculation in the order in which it is given.

Example

$z = 1 + 2 \times (11 - 4)$

The operations are + (i.e. A), × (i.e. M) and () (i.e. B)
The order of operation is B(od)MA(s)
Therefore if we have $z = 1 + 2 \times (11 - 4)$

			Key sequence
B: $(11 - 4)$	$= 7$		off on 1 1 − 4 =
M: 2×7	$= 14$		× 2 =
A: $1 + 14$	$= 15$		+ 1 =
z	$= 15$		

(If we had used the key sequence 1 + 2 × 1 1 − 4 = , the incorrect answer given would have been 29.)

Example

  p = 8 + 7 ÷ 4

The operations are A and D

The order of operations is (bo)D(m)A(s)

  D: 7 ÷ 4 = 1.75   off on 7 ÷ 4 =

  A: 8 + 1.75 = 9.75   + 8 =

            p = 9.75

Remember, too, that a fraction means division:

$$\frac{3}{4} \text{ means } 3 \div 4, \quad \frac{6}{21} \text{ means } 6 \div 21$$

Example

$$y = \frac{15}{24} + 4 \times 3 = 15 \div 24 + 4 \times 3$$

The operations are DAM

The order of operations is (bo)DMA(s)

  D: 15 ÷ 24 = 0.625 (remember this)

                 off on 1 5 ÷ 2 4 = M+

  M: 4 × 3 = 12   4 × 3 =

  A: 0.625 + 12 = 12.625   + MRC =

Strictly speaking, you do not need to press = between each stage, although if you **do** press = you will always get the correct answer.

Try   off on 1 1 − 4 = × 2 = + 1 =

and   off on 1 1 − 4 × 2 + 1 =

Try   off on 7 ÷ 4 = + 8 =

and   off on 7 ÷ 4 + 8 =

Try

off on 1 5 ÷ 2 4 = M+ 4 × 3 = + MRC =

and

off on 1 5 ÷ 2 4 M+ 4 × 3 + MRC =

Check 4

What is the 'word' which helps us to remember the order of doing different calculations?
Fill in the answers in the table. The first problem has been filled in as an example. (You do not need to do any actual calculations.)

Expression	Operations	Order of operations
$r - (p - q)$	S, B	B, S
$a \times b - c$		
$3 \times (5 + 6)$		
$3 \times 5 + 6$		
$x \div y + z$		
$x - y \div z$		
$a + (b - d) \times c$		
$33 - (5 - 2) \times 7$		
$5.6 + (3.1 - 1.4) \times 4.1$		
$b \times a + \dfrac{c}{d}$		
$b - \dfrac{c}{d}$		

T A K E   A   B R E A K   N O W

Let's return now to feeding our babies! So far we have not considered Peter. This is because he was born prematurely and is very underweight.

How much fluid does Peter require according to his weight?

1. Formula: Daily fluid requirement in ml = 150 × Weight in kg
2. Number: 1.75 kg
3. Put number in formula: Fluid requirement = 150 × 1.75 = 262.5 ml
4. If he is fed according to his weight he will be given these small feeds and this will hold him back from reaching the normal weight for a child of his age.

A normal baby's weight gain is given by the following table:

Infant's age in months	Normal weight gain in grams per week
½*–3	200
3–6	150
6–9	100
9–12	50–75
12–24	2.5 kg over the year

*During the first week of life a baby loses weight, but should have regained his birth weight by the end of the second week.

There is a formula for calculating what a baby should weigh (this is probably the most complicated formula you will ever use).

Expected weight (kg) = Birth weight (kg) +

(Age in **weeks** − 2) × Normal weight gain (kg)

How much **should** Peter weigh?

1. Formula for expected weight is given on previous page.
2. Numbers: Birth weight = 1.8 kg; age = 3 weeks; normal gain = 200 g = 0.2 kg
3. Put the numbers in the formula:

   Expected weight   = 1.8 + (3 − 2) × 0.2 kg

   Key sequence

   | off | on | 3 | − | 2 | × | 0 | . | 2 | + | 1 | . | 8 | = |

   = 2 kg
4. Peter should weigh 2 kg, but in fact he only weighs 1.75 kg.

It would probably be a good idea to feed Peter according to his expected weight in order to help him gain weight more rapidly.

How much should Peter have per day?
1. Formula: Fluid required = 150 × **Expected** weight
2. Number: Expected weight = 2 kg
3. Put number in formula: Fluid requirement
        = 150 × 2 ml
        = 300 ml
4. Peter should be offered about 300 ml per day, but owing to his being premature he might not be able to take the full amount of the extra 37.5 ml.

We can now check whether Sarah has gained a sufficient amount since birth.

1. Formula: Expected weight = Birth weight + (Age in weeks − 2) × normal gain in kg
2. Numbers: Birth weight = 3.2 kg; age = 4 weeks; normal gain = 0.2 kg
3. Put numbers in formula:

   Expected weight   = 3.2 + (4 − 2) × 0.2 kg

   Key sequence

   | off | on | 4 | − | 2 | × | 0 | . | 2 | + | 3 | . | 2 | = |

   = 3.6 kg
4. Sarah is in fact a little overweight.

Example

Amanda, age 5 months, has been admitted to hospital with a stomach disorder. She weighed 5.2 kg at 3 months old and now weighs 5.9 kg. Is this a satisfactory weight?

In this situation we do not know Amanda's birth weight so we cannot use the formula we have used so far. We need to know a formula based on weight at 3 months old. The formula is:

Expected weight (kg) = Weight at 3 months (kg) +

(Age in weeks − 12) × Normal weight gain (kg)

(Don't panic—you are not expected to remember this formula!)

Right:
1. Formula: As given above.
2. Numbers: 3-month weight = 5.2 kg; age in weeks = 20; and normal weight gain = ?
   Be careful here, we are considering a 5-month-old child so we must take the value from the table which quotes normal weight gain corresponding to a 3–6-month-old child.
   So, normal weight gain = 150 g = 0.15 kg.
3. Put numbers in formula:

   Expected weight   = 5.2 + (20 − 12) × 0.15 kg

   Key sequence

   | off | on | 2 | 0 | − | 1 | 2 | × | 0 | . | 1 | 5 | + | 5 | . | 2 | = |

   = 6.4 kg
4. Amanda is 0.5 kg underweight.

Check 5

The formulae you need are given at the foot of this page and the details from the record card for the babies are on page 84.

Have Robert, Mary and Tom made satisfactory weight gains since birth?

If Elizabeth weighed 6 kg at 4 months old, has she progressed satisfactorily over the last 2 months? Use the formula:

Expected weight = Weight at 4 months + (Age in weeks − 16) × Normal weight gain in kg

Be careful with the normal weight gain! Use the table given below. Assume a month is 4 weeks.

Infant's age in months	Normal weight gain in grams per week
½–3	200
3–6	150
6–9	100
9–12	50–75

Formulae

Quantity given at each feed =

$$\frac{\text{Recommended daily requirement}}{\text{Number of feeds per day}}$$

Daily fluid requirement in ml = 150 × Weight in kg

Expected weight in kg = Birth weight in kg + (Age in weeks − 2) × Normal weight gain in kg

For underweight babies: Fluid required in ml = 150 × Expected weight in kg

Sometimes you will need to decide which of the formulae from the list you need to use.

A new baby, Angela, is brought into the ward. Angela is 7 weeks old and weighs 3.8 kg. Her birth weight was 3.2 kg. We need to work out how much to feed her at each of 5 meal times.

First we should check whether she has been gaining weight satisfactorily. (You usually need to do this for a young child in hospital because the fact that she is not well often indicates that she has not been gaining weight satisfactorily.)

Look at the formulae on the previous page.

1. Formula: Expected weight = Birth weight + (Age in weeks − 2) × Normal weight gain
2. Numbers: Birth weight = 3.2 kg; age = 7 weeks; normal weight gain = 0.2 kg
3. Put numbers in formula: Expected weight = 3.2 + (7 − 2) × 0.2 kg = 4.2 kg
4. Her expected weight is 4.2 kg, but she only weighs 3.8 kg, so we should calculate her fluid requirement based on her expected weight.

How much fluid does Angela need each day?

1. Formula: Daily fluid requirement = 150 × Expected weight in kg
2. Number: Expected weight = 4.2 kg
3. Put number in formula: Daily fluid requirement = 150 × 4.2 = 630 ml
4. Angela should be given 650 ml a day.

How much does she need at each meal?

1. Formula: Quantity for each feed

$$= \frac{\text{Recommended daily requirement}}{\text{Number of meals per day}}$$

2. Numbers: Daily requirement = 650 ml; number of meals = 5

3. Put numbers in formula: Quantity for each feed

$$= \frac{650}{5} = 130 \text{ ml}$$

4. Angela should be offered 130 ml per feed.

Check 6

William is 11 weeks old and weighs 4 kg. His birth weight was 3.1 kg. (Use the formulae on page 100.)

How much should he weigh?

How much should he be fed each day?

If he has 6 meals a day, how much should he be offered at each feed?

TAKE A BREAK NOW

So far we have worked only with word formulae. Occasionally you will meet formulae expressed in algebraic form. You solve these by using exactly the same 4 stages that you used for word formulae.

Problem

$$D = \frac{A}{(A + 12)} \qquad \text{Find D when A} = 3$$

1. Choose formula: $D = \dfrac{A}{(A + 12)}$

2. Choose number: $A = 3$

3. Put number in formula:

$$D = \frac{3}{(3 + 12)}$$
$$= 3 \div (3 + 12)$$

Key sequence

[off] [on] [3] [+] [1] [2] [M+] [3] [÷] [MRC] [=]

$$D = 0.2$$

4. Understanding the answer: since we do not know what A and D represent we can do nothing more with the answer. (In fact it is a formula which used to be used to calculate the portion of an adult drug dose which should be given to a 3-year-old child.)

Another problem

$$E = b + (c - 2) \times g \qquad \text{Find E when b} = 3, c = 8,$$
$$g = 0.2$$

1. Formula: $E = b + (c - 2) \times g$
2. Numbers: $b = 3$; $c = 8$; $g = 0.2$
3. Put numbers in formula: $E = 3 + (8 - 2) \times 0.2 = 4.2$
4. Understand the answer: $E = 4.2$. You may have spotted that this is in fact the expected weight formula for an 8-week-old baby with birth weight 3 kg.

Check 7

The only common algebraic formulae you are likely to need in nursing are those for converting temperatures from Fahrenheit to Celsius and vice versa. (You do not need to remember them at this stage.) Find the temperature in Fahrenheit (F) if the temperature is 20° Celsius.
Use the formula:

$$F = C \times \frac{9}{5} + 32$$

Find the Celsius temperature (C) if F = 95.
Use the formula:

$$C = (F - 32) \times \frac{5}{9}$$

There is one more area in nursing which requires some use of formulae, and that is the calculation of drug doses using stock medicines which are not always in the strength you want.

There is a separate unit covering all the difficulties involved in calculating drug doses but it is worthwhile looking briefly at one of the formulae (not the best!) which you may come across. It is used here **only** as an example of working with unfamiliar formulae.

Dose given =

$$\frac{\text{Strength prescribed}}{\text{Strength available in stock}} \times \text{Dose prescribed}$$

Consider this problem:

The doctor prescribes 1 ml of drug solution strength 300 micrograms per ml. The stock bottle in the ward has 600 micrograms per ml. How much should you give to the patient?

Just follow the rules:

1. Formula: Dose given =

$$\frac{\text{Strength prescribed}}{\text{Strength available in stock}} \times \text{Dose prescribed}$$

2. Numbers:
   Strength prescribed = 300 micrograms/ml
   Strength available = 600 micrograms/ml
   Dose prescribed = 1 ml

3. Put numbers in formula:

$$\text{Dose given} = \frac{300}{600} \times 1 = 0.5 \text{ ml}$$

4. Understand the answer: you will give the patient 0.5 ml from the bottle strength 600 micrograms/ml in your ward stock cupboard.

Look at another drug dose example:

The doctor prescribes 40 mg of ointment of strength 5 mg/g. The dispensary only has ointment of strength 8 mg/g. How much should be used?

1. Formula: Dose given =

$$\frac{\text{Strength prescribed}}{\text{Strength available}} \times \text{Dose prescribed}$$

2. Numbers: Strength prescribed = 5 mg/g; strength available = 8 mg/g; dose prescribed = 40 mg

3. Put numbers in formula:

$$\text{Dose to be used} = \frac{5}{8} \times 40 \text{ mg} = 25 \text{ mg}$$

4. In this case you cannot just give a patient a stronger ointment since it might be harmful to the skin. The dispenser would take 25 mg of the stock ointment and mix it with 15 mg of, for example, cold cream to dilute the strength to that prescribed by the doctor.

Summary

You have now worked with all the types of formulae you will meet as a nurse. The important thing to remember is the 4 stages:

1. Choose the formula
2. Choose the numbers
3. Put the numbers in the formula
4. Understand the answer

Stage 1 causes few problems in practice. You will either be using a formula so often that after a while you have no problem remembering it, or will be told which formula to use by a senior nurse.

Stage 2 needs a little more thought. You have to select values to put in the formula from record cards, lists, tables, etc. **Be careful with the units.**

Stage 3 merely involves putting the numbers in the right places and doing some arithmetic—**carefully**.

Stage 4 should **never** be missed out. Anyone can make a mistake in stage 3. Only by looking at the number you have for an answer and thinking what it means will you be able to spot the errors you have made. Always ask yourself: **Is that a sensible answer?**

Now look back through the unit to refresh your memory and then turn over for the final check test.

Final check

1) $F = C \times \dfrac{9}{5} + 32$ Find F if C = 15

2) $N = B + 150 \times A - 300$ Find N if B = 3.5
    and A = 4

For questions 3 to 6 use the following formulae:

Quantity for each feed in ml

$$= \frac{\text{Daily fluid requirement in ml}}{\text{Number of feeds per day}}$$

Daily fluid requirement in ml = 150 × Weight in kg

For underweight babies: Daily fluid requirement in ml = 150 × Expected weight in kg

Expected weight in kg = Birth weight + (Age in weeks − 2) × Normal weight gain in kg

Normal weight gain from 2 weeks to 3 months is 200 g per week

Dose given = $\dfrac{\text{Strength prescribed}}{\text{Strength available}}$ × Dose prescribed

Lorna, age 2½ months, is brought into hospital weighing 4.5 kg. Her birth weight was 3.8 kg.

3) How much should she weigh?
4) How much fluid should she be given each day?
5) How much fluid should she be given at each of 5 feeds?
6) Lorna is prescribed 10 ml of ampicillin strength 50 mg per ml, but the ward stock strength is 100 mg per ml. How many ml of ampicillin should she be given from the ward stock?

Answers

Check 1

4 stages

1) Choose the right formula.
2) Choose the right numbers.
3) Put the numbers in the right places in the formula.
4) Know how to use the answer.

Check 2

Tom: 125 ml
Mary: 181.25 ml, but offer her 180–200 ml
Although Robert and Mary have the same recommended daily intake, Mary needs more at each feed because she is only having 4 meals whereas Robert is having 5 meals.

Check 3

Robert: 720 ml so the record card recommendation is OK.
Tom: 750 ml so the record card recommendation is OK.

Check 4

BODMAS

Operations	Order of operations
M, S	M, S
M, B	B, M
M, A	M, A
D, A	D, A
S, D	D, S
A, B, M	B, M, A
S, B, M	B, M, S
A, B, M	B, M, A
M, A, D	D, M, A
S, D	D, S

Check 5

	Expected weight (kg)	Comment
Robert	4.7	OK
Mary	4.3	Rather overweight
Tom	4.8	A little overweight
Elizabeth	Between 6.8 and 7.2	OK

Check 6

Expected weight 4.9 kg
Daily fluid requirement 735 ml, but offer him 750 ml
At each feed give 125 ml

Check 7

$F = 68$
$C = 35$

Final check

1) $F = 59$
2) $N = 303.5$
3) Expected weight $= 5.4$ kg
4) Daily fluid $= 810$ ml
5) At each meal give 162 ml, but offer 175 ml
6) Dose $= 5$ ml

U N I T 4

Percentages

'Per cent' means 'in every 100'. 'Cent' nearly always indicates a relationship with 100. Century means 100 years. A centipede has 100 legs or thereabouts!

The symbol for per cent is %.

'Eleven per cent of learner nurses are male' means that out of every hundred learners, 11 will be male (and therefore, 89 will be female). Another way of expressing this percentage is to say 'eleven hundredths $\left(\dfrac{11}{100}\right)$ of the total number of learner nurses are male (and therefore $\dfrac{(100 - 11)}{100} = \dfrac{89}{100}$ are female)'.

'Fifty three per cent of nurses are married by the end of their training' means that out of every 100 nurses, 53 will have found a husband (or wife) by the end of their training. In other words, $\dfrac{53}{100}$ of the total number of learners will be married, and $\dfrac{(100 - 53)}{100} = \dfrac{47}{100}$ of the total number of learners will still be single at the end of their training.

You will frequently meet percentages as labels for substances. For example, 'a 20% disinfectant solution' means that every 100 ml of the solution contains 20 ml disinfectant and 80 ml of water. When you read '5% dextrose in water' it means that every 100 ml of solution contains 5 ml dextrose and 95 ml water.

In other words, if you have a litre of 20% disinfectant, $\frac{20}{100}$ of the litre is pure disinfectant and $\frac{80}{100}$ of the litre is water. If you have one millilitre of 5% dextrose, then $\frac{5}{100}$ ml is dextrose and $\frac{95}{100}$ ml is water. Similarly, a millilitre of 7.5% solution contains $\frac{7.5}{100}$ ml drug and $\frac{92.5}{100}$ ml of whatever it is dissolved in (the *solvent*).

Do not be put off or flustered by unfamiliar drug names or complicated looking numbers.

A '2.25% solution of propanidid' just means $\frac{2.25}{100}$ units of pure drug and $\frac{(100 - 2.25)}{100} = \frac{97.75}{100}$ units of solvent. 'A subcutaneous injection of 0.18% sodium chloride solution with hyaluronidase' means $\frac{0.18}{100}$ units of sodium chloride (salt) and $\frac{(100 - 0.18)}{100} = \frac{99.82}{100}$ units of hyaluronidase solution.

Check 1

Explain the meaning of the following:

  5% sodium bicarbonate solution
  2.5% saline (salt) solution
  1 ml thiopentone given intravenously in a 2.5% solution

How much disinfectant is there in a litre of 25% solution?

How much water?

As a nurse you will have to be able to do a couple of things with percentages.

(i) You must understand the meaning of % (you have just learned this!) and have an idea of 'size' related to percentages.

(ii) You may well have to calculate simple percentages in order to give a certain drug dose or to mix up a solution of a particular strength.

Let's look at (i) first, i.e. 'size'.

Per cent, or %, means 'in every hundred'. If we have two bottles of dextrose in water solution, one labelled '5% dextrose' and the other labelled '50% dextrose', what can we say to compare the two solutions?

5% dextrose means 5 ml of dextrose in each 100 ml of solution

50% dextrose means 50 ml of dextrose in each 100 ml of solution

Clearly the second solution contains much more dextrose, in fact, 10 times as much as the first bottle.

Which is stronger, hydrocortisone eye-drops (1% acetate) or hydrocortisone eye ointment (2.5% acetate)?

One hundred units of the eye-drops contain 1 unit of hydrocortisone acetate while the 100 units of the ointment contain 2.5 units of hydrocortisone acetate and this is therefore a stronger preparation.

Check 2

Thiopentone (an anaesthetic) can be used in a 2.5% solution or in a 5% solution. Which is the stronger dose?

Which of the following diagnostic injections contains the least diodone:

a 35, 50 or 70 per cent solution?

Now let's consider (ii), i.e. percentage calculations.*

To do actual calculations with percentages is simple as long as you remember the meaning of per cent.

The most common solutions you will have to make up will be disinfectants. Chloroxylenol is one such disinfectant—Dettol is a particular brand name.

Consider a 10% solution:

To make a 10% solution of chloroxylenol, you will need 10 ml of chloroxylenol and 90 ml of solvent (in this case water) to get 100 ml of 10% solution

or 10 litres chloroxylenol and 90 litres of water to get 100 litres of 10% solution
or 10 teaspoons chloroxylenol and 90 teaspoons of water to get 100 teaspoons of 10% solution
or 10 buckets chloroxylenol and 90 buckets of water to get 100 buckets of 10% solution

No matter how you measure your disinfectant, you need 10 units of disinfectant to every 90 units of water to get 100 units of a 10% solution.

NB: The percentage number (e.g. '10' in 10%) always gives the quantity of pure drug and '100 minus the percentage number' (e.g. $100 - 10 = 90$ for a 10% solution) gives the quantity of solvent.

---

*Your calculator has a $\boxed{\%}$ button. The safest thing to do is ignore it! For those of you who are curious, its use is explained on page 125.

Check 3

What quantity of pure drug is needed to make up 100 ml of 25% solution?

How much solvent must be added?

How many tablespoons of concentrated orange juice are needed to mix up 100 spoonfuls of 12% solution?

How much water is needed?

So far, we know that, no matter what units or what drugs we use

100 units of a 25% solution contains 25 units of pure drug and 75 units of solvent.

Problem

What if we want only one unit of a 25% solution?

On page 112 we saw that another way of writing '11% of learners are male' was to say '$\frac{11}{100}$ of the **total** number of learners are male'.

Here the 'total' quantity we are considering is one unit so:

One unit of a 25% solution has $\frac{25^\star}{100}$ of a unit of pure drug and $\frac{75}{100}$ of a unit of solvent—**whatever the units are**.

Example

1 ml of 5% dextrose contains $\frac{5}{100}$ ml of dextrose and $\frac{95}{100}$ ml of water.

Example

Consider methoxyflurane, 0.35%, a gas given by midwives to patients during labour. (Do not be put off by the name or the number! Just apply the rules.)

1 litre of methoxyflurane 0.35% in air contains $\frac{0.35}{100}$ litres of the gas and $\frac{99.65}{100}$ litres of air.

$\star$(Hint: do **not** be tempted to cancel the 100 with any other part of the calculation. A fraction with 100 on the bottom is very easy to convert to a decimal, with or without your calculator.)

Check 4

How much undiluted Roxenol (disinfectant) is needed to make up 1 litre of 2% solution?

How much water?

How much chlorhexidine is needed to make 1 g of 1% antiseptic cream?

How much cream base?

Noradrenaline is a hormone used in the treatment of shock. It is given in a 0.1% solution. So 1 ml of the 0.1% noradrenaline contains $\dfrac{0.1}{100}$ ml of hormone and $\dfrac{99.9}{100}$ ml of solvent.

The normal dose, however, comes in an ampoule containing not 1 ml but 4 ml. How much hormone is there, therefore, in the ampoule?

1 ml contains $\dfrac{0.1}{100}$ ml of hormone, therefore:

4 ml contains $4 \times \dfrac{0.1}{100}$ ml of hormone

Key sequence

| off | on | 0 | . | 1 | ÷ | 1 | 0 | 0 | × | 4 | = |

= 0.004 ml

Similarly

2 ml contains $2 \times \dfrac{0.1}{100}$ ml of hormone = 0.002 ml

Example

We have 500 ml of 5% dextrose for use as a drip. How much dextrose will the patient be given?

1 ml contains $\dfrac{5}{100}$ ml of dextrose

so 500 ml contains $500 \times \dfrac{5}{100}$ ml of dextrose = 25 ml

Example

A 5 mg tube of 7.5% antiseptic cream is given to a patient. How much pure antiseptic is used?

1 mg contains $\dfrac{7.5}{100}$ mg of pure antiseptic

so 5 mg contains $5 \times \dfrac{7.5}{100}$ mg of pure antiseptic

= 0.375 mg of pure antiseptic

You may have met other methods of calculating percentages, but this method will **always** enable you to make up solutions of a specified strength and to calculate the amount of pure drug in any given solution.

Check 5

What quantities of pure drug and water are needed to make up 100 ml of 15% solution?

How much dextrose is needed to make 1 litre of 5% solution?

How much water is needed for a litre of 25% saline solution?

How much lignocaine is needed for 200 ml of 2% solution?

How much drug is there in:

   1 litre of 1.36% dextrose solution?
   2 ml of 60% solution of Triosil?
   7.5 ml of 12% solution of sodium iodide?

Summary

Per cent means 'in every hundred'. A 5% saline solution means 5 parts of salt and 95 parts of water in every 100 parts of solution.

The higher the percentage number the stronger the solution. 40% solution is stronger than 10% solution.

To calculate the quantity of drug in 40 ml of 5% solution:

First calculate the quantity in 1 ml of 5% solution: 1 ml contains $\dfrac{5}{100}$ ml of drug, then calculate the quantity for 40 ml:

40 ml contains $40 \times \dfrac{5}{100}$ ml of drug.

Final check

Explain what is meant when a urine sample is said to contain 2% sugar.

A second urine sample contains 1% sugar. Describe what is happening to the sugar level of this patient.

Calculate the quantity of drug needed to make:

   1 litre of 5% solution
   5 litres of 7% solution
   2.5 litres of 10% solution
   4 ml of 12.5% solution

Percentage on the calculator

Consider the situation where we wish to know how much dextrose there is in 300 ml of 5% solution.

1 ml of 5% solution contains $\dfrac{5}{100}$ ml of dextrose

so 300 ml of 5% solution contains $300 \times \dfrac{5}{100}$ ml of dextrose

Use the calculator key sequence

[off][on][5][÷][1][0][0][×][3][0][0][=]

The answer is 15.

There are 15 ml of pure dextrose in 300 ml of 5% solution.

This is a reasonable answer.

Now try the calculation using the % button.

Use the key sequence [off][on][3][0][0][×][5][%][=]

The answer is 4500

There are 4500 ml of dextrose in 300 ml of solution! Nonsense!

Try the key sequence again and watch the display **carefully**.

The answer '15' appears **before** you press [=] .

Since the temptation is always to press [=] after any calculation, it is much safer not to use the [%] key method.

A further problem arises if you wish to calculate 25% of 200.

This means $\dfrac{25}{100}$ of 200, so use the key sequence

[2][5][÷][1][0][0][×][2][0][0][=]

The answer is 50. Correct.

Now try the key sequence [2][5][%][×][2][0][0][=]

The answer is 0!

The display before pressing [=] was 200 so that was not right either!

You are strongly advised to ignore the [%] key.

Answers

Check 1

$\dfrac{5}{100}$ sodium bicarbonate and $\dfrac{95}{100}$ water

$\dfrac{2.5}{100}$ salt and $\dfrac{97.5}{100}$ water

$\dfrac{2.5}{100}$ ml thiopentone and $\dfrac{97.5}{100}$ sterile water

$\dfrac{25}{100}$ litre or 0.25 l or ¼ l disinfectant

$\dfrac{75}{100}$ litre or 0.75 l or ¾ l water

Check 2

5% is twice as strong
35% contains least diodone

Check 3

25 ml drug
75 ml solvent

12 tbs
88 tbs

Check 4

$\dfrac{2}{100}$ litre or 0.02 l or 20 ml

$\dfrac{98}{100}$ litre or 0.98 l or 980 ml

$\dfrac{1}{100}$ g or 0.01 g or 10 mg

$\dfrac{99}{100}$ g or 0.99 g or 990 mg

Check 5

15 ml drug and 85 ml water

$\dfrac{5}{100}$ l or 0.05 l or 50 ml dextrose

$\dfrac{75}{100}$ l or 0.75 l or 750 ml water

$200 \times \dfrac{2}{100}$ ml = 4 ml lignocaine

0.0136 l (or 13.6 ml)
1.2 ml Triosil
0.9 ml sodium iodide

Final check

The sample of urine contains 2 ml sugar in every 100 ml urine.

1% is less concentrated than 2%, so the sugar level is falling. The second sample is in fact half the strength of the first sample.

$\dfrac{5}{100}$ l or 0.05 l or 50 ml

$\dfrac{35}{100}$ l or 0.35 l or 350 ml

$\dfrac{25}{100}$ l or 0.25 l or 250 ml

$\dfrac{50}{100}$ ml or 0.5 ml

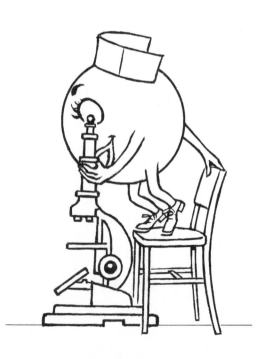

Indices

An index number (plural is indices) is the number which says how many times a figure (called the base number) is multiplied together with itself.

Let us look at an example: 7^2

The little 2 is the index number. It means that 2 of the base number 7 are multiplied together. In other words
$7^2 = 7 \times 7 = 49$

Consider 4^3:

The 3 is the index number and means that $4^3 = 4 \times 4 \times 4 = 64$. Similarly, $2^8 = 2 \times 2 \times 2 \times 2 \times 2 \times 2 \times 2 \times 2 = 256$. And logically, 5^1 (index number 1) = 5. Index 1 implies only one five to give the answer.

Check 1

What is the base number in 2^3, 5^2, 3^{10}, 10^3?

What is the index number (or power) in 2^3, 5^2, 3^{10}, 10^3?

Write out and calculate
$$3^4 =$$
$$10^2 =$$
$$7^1 =$$
$$1^6 = \quad \text{(Be careful)}$$
$$2^3 =$$
$$3^2 =$$

Now consider the following numbers and indices:

2^1, 2^2, 2^3, 2^4, 2^5, 2^6: these numbers are all in index form with base number 2

$2^1 = 2$

$2^2 = 2 \times 2 = 4$

$2^3 = 2 \times 2 \times 2 = 8$

$2^4 = 2 \times 2 \times 2 \times 2 = 16$

$2^5 = 2 \times 2 \times 2 \times 2 \times 2 = 32$

$2^6 = 2 \times 2 \times 2 \times 2 \times 2 \times 2 = 64$

Notice the base number (2) is the same for all the numbers and as the index gets larger (1, 2, 3, 4, 5, 6) so does the answer (2, 4, 8, 16, 32, 64).

This means that we can put numbers in index form **with the same base** in order of size without working out the multiplication. This can be very useful as you will see later. (Most dodges to avoid long multiplication are useful!)

Example

Put 6^3, 6^{12}, 6^1, 6^7 in order of size with the largest first. The base number is 6 in each case so we need only consider the order of the indices, and we get

6^{12}, 6^7, 6^3, 6^1.

You can **only** do this when the base number is the same throughout.

Check 2

Which is the larger 4^{10} or 4^5? Why?

Put the following in order of size, with the largest first and without doing the multiplication.

$7^9, 7^2, 7^4, 7^1$
$12^7, 12^{206}, 12^1, 12^{99}$

Can you put the following in order of size with the largest first and without doing the multiplication?

$2^3, 3^5, 9^2$?
Give a reason for your answer.

Can you put the following in order of size with the largest first and without doing the multiplication?

$10^2, 10^5, 5^2, 10^7$

Let us now look at numbers in index form with the same index number, but different base numbers.

$2^3, 3^3, 4^3, 5^3$
$2^3 = 2 \times 2 \times 2 = 8$
$3^3 = 3 \times 3 \times 3 = 27$
$4^3 = 4 \times 4 \times 4 = 64$
$5^3 = 5 \times 5 \times 5 = 125$

Notice that the index number (3) is the same for all the numbers and as the base number gets larger (2, 3, 4, 5) so the answers get larger (8, 27, 64, 125). This means that we can put numbers in index form with the **same index number** in order of size without working out the multiplication.

Example

Put $5^4, 2^4, 3^4, 10^4, 1^4$ in order of size with the smallest first.

The index number (4) is the same for all the numbers so we need only consider the order of the base numbers. We get

$1^4, 2^4, 3^4, 5^4, 10^4$.

You can **only** do this when the index is the same throughout.

Check 3

Which is the larger 8^{92} or 3^{92}?

Put the following in order of size with the largest first and without doing the multiplication.

$7^4, 5^4, 16^4, 1^4$
$206^9, 906^9, 602^9, 620^9$

Can you put the following in order of size with the largest first and without doing the multiplication?

$5^3, 6^2, 14^1, 305^2$
Give a reason for your answer.

Can you put the following in order of size with the smallest first and without doing the multiplication?

      $6^5, 7^5, 5^3, 3^5, 19^5$ Why?
or $8^3, 11^3, 3, 7^3$ Why?

TAKE A BREAK NOW

A nurse rarely (if ever?) has to work out unpleasant arithmetic such as 23^{19} or even 7^5. However, a nurse **does** need to be able to look at path. lab. reports and decide whether a doctor should be informed immediately, soon, or on his or her next visit.

If a blood sample is sent for analysis one of the pathology technician's jobs may well be to count the number of red or white cells present in the blood. This, for means of standard comparison, is always given as a number of cells per litre. Trouble arises with this form of reporting because there are possibly five thousand million (5 000 000 000) white cells and one thousand times **more** (5 000 000 000 000) red cells in a litre of blood.

Obviously there is a great danger with these very large numbers of the lab. technician mis-writing or the nurse mis-counting the number of zeros. Some safer method is needed. A system of number writing called 'standard form' is the ideal solution. We will now look at how this works.

Let us first look at simple numbers with several zeros:

10, 100, 1000, 10000, 1000000000000

We can rewrite these numbers as multiples (or *powers*) of 10 and then express them in index form.

$$
\begin{aligned}
10 &= 10^1 \\
100 &= 10 \times 10 = 10^2 \\
1000 &= 10 \times 10 \times 10 = 10^3 \\
10000 &= 10 \times 10 \times 10 \times 10 = 10^4 \\
1000000000000 &= 10 \times 10 \times 10 \times 10 \times 10 \times 10 \times 10 \\
&\quad \times 10 \times 10 \times 10 \times 10 \times 10 \\
&= 10^{12}
\end{aligned}
$$

So we can write one thousand million as 10^9 (one 'ten' for each zero).

Check 4

Can you remember how many white cells a litre of blood may have?

Why are blood cell counts given as 'so many per litre'?

Put the following in index form:

100
1000000
100000
10000000000
1000000000000000

That is a fine method for exact powers of ten, but life is not that simple.

Consider 500:

We know that $100 = 10^2$. Is 500 the same as 5^2? **No**

$5^2 = 5 \times 5 = 25$ so that won't do.

Suppose we write $500 = 5 \times 100$

We can then say $500 = 5 \times 10^2$

What about 3000?

We know that $1000 = 10 \times 10 \times 10 = 10^3$. Is 3000 the same as 3^3? **No**

$3^3 = 3 \times 3 \times 3 = 27$ so that won't do.

But if we write $3000 = 3 \times 1000$

We can then write $3000 = 3 \times 10^3$

Can we use this for all such numbers?

Let us look at a further example:

What about 20000000?

$10000000 = 10 \times 10 \times 10 \times 10 \times 10 \times 10 \times 10$
$= 10^7$

But $2^7 = 2 \times 2 \times 2 \times 2 \times 2 \times 2 \times 2 = 128$. No good.

However, $20000000 = 2 \times 10000000$
$= 2 \times 10^7$

We call this method of writing numbers *standard form*.

Thus 70000 in standard form is 7×10^4

9000000 in standard form is 9×10^6

30 in standard form is 3×10^1 (or just 3×10)

Check 5

Write the following in standard form.
900
40000
50
600000000000

We can, in fact, use this method of writing numbers using powers of 10 for all numbers.

Now $20 = 2 \times 10$. OK
If we want to do the same thing with 5 we could say
$5 = 0.5 \times 10$

This looks like an odd thing to do, but you will see how it actually simplifies the situation.

Consider 25.
$25 = 20 + 5$
$\quad = 2 \times 10 + 0.5 \times 10$
$\quad = (2 + 0.5) \times 10$
So we have $25 = 2.5 \times 10$ and therefore 25 in standard form is written as 2.5×10.

What about 361?
$361 = 300 + 60 + 1$
$\quad = 3 \times 10^2 + 0.6 \times 10^2 + 0.01 \times 10^2$

[We need the powers of 10 to be the same (i.e. 10^2 for all the bits of 361) otherwise we cannot now put them together.]

Thus $361 = (3 + 0.6 + 0.01) \times 10^2$
$= 3.61 \times 10^2$

So in standard form

$$361 = 3.61 \times 10^2$$
$$\text{Similarly } 983 = 9.83 \times 10^2$$
$$5644 = 5.644 \times 10^3$$
$$21033 = 2.1033 \times 10^4$$

In other words, to put a number in standard form, change it to a decimal with one whole number (e.g. for 798 write 7.98) and multiply by a power of 10 (e.g. 10^2). The index number for the 10 is given by counting the number of figures after the decimal point, **including any zeros**.

Examples

$$430 \text{ is } 4.30 \times 10^2 \text{ in standard form.}$$
$$22000 \text{ is } 2.2000 \times 10^4 \text{ in standard form.}$$
$$5000260 \text{ is } 5.000260 \times 10^6 \text{ in standard form.}$$

Check 6

Write the following in standard form.

29
7604
299
261000
35000
96400000
5707000000

TAKE A BREAK NOW

Nurses need to be able to do only one thing with numbers in standard form. That is, to compare them.

There are two possible situations for comparison.

1. Is 5.6×10^8 larger or smaller than 5.6×10^7?
2. Is 8.73×10^{12} larger or smaller than 9.88×10^{12}?

Situation 1

In this situation we have the same decimal number multiplied by different powers of 10. We know that if we have the same base number we can order numbers by the index, so

10^8 is larger than 10^7 (base number 10; indices 8 and 7), and 5.6×10^8 is larger than 5.6×10^7.

In fact we can go further than this and say that if, and only if, numbers are written in standard form we can order them merely by ordering the indices because the base number is always 10 and the decimal number is between 1 and 10.

Example

5.3×10^7 and 2.4×10^8.
Ignore the decimal number. The base number is 10 in both, and 8 is larger than 7, so

2.4×10^8 is larger than 5.3×10^7.

Example

Which is the larger? 2.294×10^3 or 9.713×10^2
The base number is 10 in both and indices are 3 and 2, so

10^3 is larger than 10^2, and therefore 2.294×10^3 is larger than 9.713×10^2

Example

Put the following in order of size, starting with the smallest.

9.6×10^3, 3.32×10^4, 8.8×10^2, 1.01×10^7

The base number is always 10 in standard form so the indices can be re-ordered 2, 3, 4, 7 giving

8.8×10^2, 9.6×10^3, 3.32×10^4, 1.01×10^7 in order of size.

Check 7

Put the following in order of size with the smallest first.

9.6×10^3, 1.5×10^2, 5.78×10^5, 2.2×10^1

2.2×10^3, 2.3×10^9, 3.2×10, 3.3×10^2

Situation 2

What happens if the base number **and** the index are the same?

2×10^2 and 3×10^2 are the standard forms for 200 and 300. The base number (10) and the index (2) are the same, but we know that 300 is bigger than 200 and that 3 is bigger than 2.

2.5×10^3 and 2.6×10^3 are the standard forms for 2500 and 2600. The base number (10) and the index (3) are the same, but we know that 2600 is bigger than 2500 and that 2.6 is bigger than 2.5.

It looks as if we can order numbers in standard form with the same power of 10 by ordering the decimal numbers. This is, in fact, the case for all numbers in standard form.

Example

Put the following in order of size, starting with the smallest.

2.38×10^9, 7.7×10^9, 4.152×10^9

All numbers are $\times 10^9$ so order the decimal numbers:

2.38, 4.152, 7.7

So 2.38×10^9, 4.152×10^9, 7.7×10^9 are in order of size, starting with the smallest.

Check 8

Put the following in order of size with the largest first.

$9.8 \times 10^{10}, 4.3 \times 10^{10}, 9.89 \times 10^{10}, 6.25 \times 10^{10}$

$1.652 \times 10^7, 3.617 \times 10^7, 1.7 \times 10^7, 1.05 \times 10^7$

Occasionally you may meet negative indices (e.g. 10^{-3}). All the facts you have learned about indices hold good for negative numbers too, as long as you remember the number line.

$$\ldots \; -5, \; -4, \; -3, \; -2, \; -1, \; 0, \; 1, \; 2, \; 3, \; 4, \; 5 \; \ldots$$

and remember that any number is smaller than any other number which is further to the right on the line.

Example

10^{-5} is smaller than 10^{-3} because -3 is to the right of -5.

To put the following in order of size with the smallest first, 2^2, 2^{-1}, 2^{-8}, 2^4, 2^{-10}, we must first order the indices as on the number line, thus

$$-10, \; -8, \; -1, \; 2, \; 4.$$

Then the number order is

$$2^{-10}, \; 2^{-8}, \; 2^{-1}, \; 2^2, \; 2^4.$$

Check 9

Put the following in order of size with the largest first.

6^2, 6^4, 6^{-5}, 6^6, 6^{-3}

10^{-1}, 10^{-3}, 10^2, 10^{10}, 10^{-7}

Now you have learned all you need to know about indices and standard form.

Summary

It is possible to put powers of **the same number** in size order by ordering the index number.

e.g. 5^2, 5^3, 5^9, 5^{263}, etc. (Powers are 2, 3, 9, 263.)

It is possible to put different numbers with the **same index number** in size order by ordering the base number.

e.g. 7^2, 13^2, 21^2, 48^2, 193^2, etc. (Base numbers 7, 13, 21, 48, 193.)

Take any number (e.g. 23640): you can write it in **standard form** (2.3640×10^4) by writing the number (23640) as a decimal with one whole number (2.3640) and multiplying by a power of 10 (10^4). The index number is always the number of figures after the decimal point **including any zeros in the original number** (.3640 has 4 figures).

Now look through the unit to refresh your memory and then turn the page and try the final check test.

Final check

Without using multiplication, where possible put the following in order of size, with the largest first.

$9^2, 7^2, 10^2, 12^2$
$3^4, 3^2, 3^{16}, 3^{111}$
$5^3, 3^5, 10^3, 5^5$
$6^2, 6^9, 6, 6^5$
$1^2, 1, 1^4, 1^{17}$

Express the following in standard form.

97200
60
411
234567890
1092873465
27000000

Put the following in order of size with the smallest first.

$7.2 \times 10^8, 6.5 \times 10^9, 4.3 \times 10^7$
$3.3 \times 10^9, 4.2 \times 10^9, 2.4 \times 10^9$

Answers

Check 1

2, 5, 3, 10
3, 2, 10, 3

$3^4 = 3 \times 3 \times 3 \times 3 = 81$
$10^2 = 10 \times 10 = 100$
$7^1 = 7$
$1^6 = 1 \times 1 \times 1 \times 1 \times 1 \times 1 = 1$
$2^3 = 2 \times 2 \times 2 = 8$
$3^2 = 3 \times 3 = 9$

Check 2

4^{10} because the base number is the same and the index 10 is larger than the index 5.

$7^9, 7^4, 7^2, 7^1$
$12^{206}, 12^{99}, 12^7, 12^1$

No, because they do not **all** have the same base number.

No, because they do not **all** have the same base number.

Check 3

8^{92}

$16^4, 7^4, 5^4, 1^4$

$906^9, 620^9, 602^9, 206^9$

No, because they do not **all** have either the same base number or the same index number.

No, because they do not **all** have either the same base number or the same index number.

No, because they do not **all** have either the same base number or the same index number.

Check 4

A litre of blood can have five thousand million white cells – don't worry if you did not remember this.

Blood counts are expressed per litre to make comparisons between samples simple.

10^2, 10^6, 10^5, 10^{10}, 10^{15}

Check 5

9×10^2
4×10^4
5×10 (or 10^1)
6×10^{11}

Check 6

2.9×10
7.604×10^3
2.99×10^2
$2.61000 \times 10^5 = 2.61 \times 10^5$
$3.5000 \times 10^4 = 3.5 \times 10^4$
$9.6400000 \times 10^7 = 9.64 \times 10^7$
$5.707000000 \times 10^9 = 5.707 \times 10^9$

You may omit the zeros on the end of the decimals as in the right hand column (2.600 is exactly the same number as 2.6). **But** only do this if you are completely confident that you understand how to get the index number.

Check 7

2.2×10^1, 1.5×10^2, 9.6×10^3, 5.78×10^5
3.2×10, 3.3×10^2, 2.2×10^3, 2.3×10^9

Check 8

9.89×10^{10}, 9.8×10^{10}, 6.25×10^{10}, 4.3×10^{10}
3.617×10^7, 1.7×10^7, 1.652×10^7, 1.05×10^7

Check 9

6^6, 6^4, 6^2, 6^{-3}, 6^{-5}
10^{10}, 10^2, 10^{-1}, 10^{-3}, 10^{-7}

Final check

12^2, 10^2, 9^2, 7^2
3^{111}, 3^{16}, 3^4, 3^2
Not possible
6^9, 6^5, 6^2, $6^{(1)}$
$1^2 = 1 = 1^4 = 1^{17}$. All powers of 1 give answer 1!

9.7200×10^4 (or 9.72×10^4)
6.0×10
4.11×10^2
2.34567890×10^8
1.092873465×10^9
2.7000000×10^7 (or 2.7×10^7)

4.3×10^7, 7.2×10^8, 6.5×10^9
2.4×10^9, 3.3×10^9, 4.2×10^9

Calculator Appendix

Square roots

To find the square root of a number you need to press the number first. Thus

$\boxed{4}$ $\boxed{\sqrt{x}}$ gives $\sqrt{4} = 2$

Percentages

To calculate 5% of 80 use the following key sequence

$\boxed{8}\boxed{0}\boxed{\times}\boxed{5}\boxed{\%}$

Very important: do not press $\boxed{=}$. You will get 80 times the answer!

Constant function

Try the following. Can you see what is happening?

Exploration 1

$\boxed{3}\boxed{+}\boxed{2}\boxed{=}$
$\boxed{3}\boxed{+}\boxed{2}\boxed{=}\boxed{=}$
$\boxed{3}\boxed{+}\boxed{2}\boxed{=}\boxed{=}\boxed{=}\boxed{=}\boxed{=}$

$\boxed{2}\boxed{7}\boxed{-}\boxed{4}\boxed{=}$
$\boxed{2}\boxed{7}\boxed{-}\boxed{4}\boxed{=}\boxed{=}$
$\boxed{2}\boxed{7}\boxed{-}\boxed{4}\boxed{=}\boxed{=}\boxed{=}$

$\boxed{8}\boxed{1}\boxed{\div}\boxed{3}\boxed{=}$
$\boxed{8}\boxed{1}\boxed{\div}\boxed{3}\boxed{=}\boxed{=}$
$\boxed{8}\boxed{1}\boxed{\div}\boxed{3}\boxed{=}\boxed{=}\boxed{=}$

$\boxed{3}\boxed{-}\boxed{2}\boxed{+}\boxed{4}\boxed{=}$
$\boxed{3}\boxed{-}\boxed{2}\boxed{+}\boxed{4}\boxed{=}\boxed{=}$
$\boxed{3}\boxed{-}\boxed{2}\boxed{+}\boxed{4}\boxed{=}\boxed{=}\boxed{=}$

$\boxed{3}\boxed{8}\boxed{-}\boxed{2}\boxed{\div}\boxed{3}\boxed{=}$
$\boxed{3}\boxed{8}\boxed{-}\boxed{2}\boxed{\div}\boxed{3}\boxed{=}\boxed{=}$

$\boxed{1}\boxed{0}\boxed{8}\boxed{\div}\boxed{6}\boxed{+}\boxed{2}\boxed{=}$
$\boxed{1}\boxed{0}\boxed{8}\boxed{\div}\boxed{6}\boxed{+}\boxed{2}\boxed{=}\boxed{=}$
$\boxed{1}\boxed{0}\boxed{8}\boxed{\div}\boxed{6}\boxed{+}\boxed{2}\boxed{=}\boxed{=}\boxed{=}$

In each case every time you press $\boxed{=}$ the calculator repeats the last function $(+, -, \div)$ and the number which follows it.

Beware! Try the following

Exploration 2

2 × 3 =
2 × 3 = =
2 × 3 = = =

1 2 × 2 =
1 2 × 2 = =
1 2 × 2 = = = =

The calculator is repeating the function and the **first** number you pressed.

Worse still! Try these:

5 × 2 × 3 =
5 × 2 × 3 = =
5 × 2 × 3 = = =

2 × 3 × 4 =
2 × 3 × 4 = =
2 × 3 × 4 = = =

9 + 1 × 2 =
9 + 1 × 2 = =
9 + 1 × 2 = = = = =

4 − 3 × 6 =
4 − 3 × 6 = =
4 − 3 × 6 = = =

The calculator is repeating the last function and the combination of all the numbers and functions before it, so that

5 + 3 − 6 × 2 × 5 becomes [5 + 3 − 6 × 2] × 5 i.e. 4 × 5

and repeated use of = gives 20, 4 × 20, 4 × 4 × 20, etc.

Powers

5 × = gives 5 × 5 i.e. 5^2
5 × = = = gives 5 × 5 × 5 × 5 i.e. 5^4

Negative numbers

These are indicated by a small − sign on the left side of the display.
4 − 7 = shows $\boxed{-\qquad 3.}$